THE WINDMILLS OF KENT

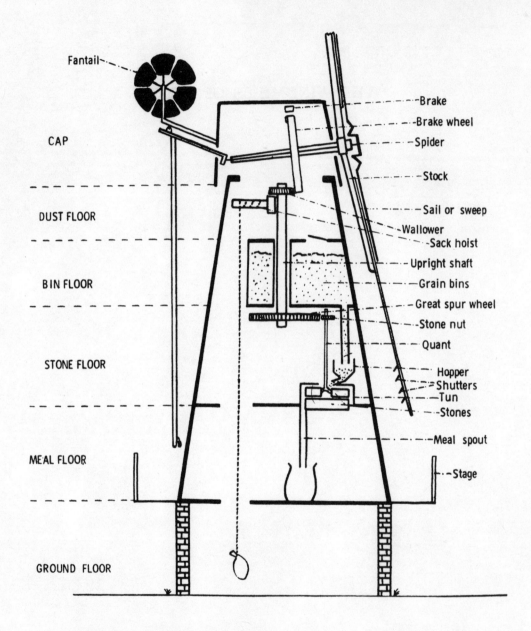

Fantail

CAP

DUST FLOOR

BIN FLOOR

STONE FLOOR

MEAL FLOOR

GROUND FLOOR

Brake
Brake wheel
Spider
Stock
Sail or sweep
Wallower
Sack hoist
Upright shaft
Grain bins
Great spur wheel
Stone nut
Quant
Hopper
Shutters
Tun
Stones
Meal spout
Stage

DIAGRAM OF TYPICAL SMOCK MILL

THE WINDMILLS
OF KENT

By JENNY WEST

WITH A FOREWORD BY
REX WAILES

SKILTON & SHAW
LONDON

To

Richard, Simon, Sarah and Sophie

First published 1973
Revised, enlarged and reprinted 1979

Printed in Great Britain for

SKILTON & SHAW
52 Lincoln's Inn Fields,
London WC2A 3NW

CONTENTS

LIST OF ILLUSTRATIONS

PHOTOGRAPHS

ACKNOWLEDGEMENTS

The research involved has required the help and co-operation of many people, to whom my thanks are due and without whom this survey would not have been possible. Names too numerous to mention individually include those owners who have enabled existing mills to be studied and photographed, and the many persons in other ways connected with, or interested in mills, who have readily imparted valuable information or lent old photographs for comparison and study.
Particular thanks are due to:

Mrs Monica Dance, Secretary, The Society for the Protection of Ancient Buildings.
Vincent Pargeter, Esq., Millwright, Ramsgate, Kent.
Arthur Stowers, Esq., Late Chairman, Wind and Watermill Section, S.P.A.B.
Rex Wailes, Esq., Chairman and Honorary Technical Advisor, Wind and Watermill Section, S.P.A.B.
Certain Kent millers, mentioned under individual mills, who have willingly shared their milling experiences.
Thanks are also due, for their helpful correspondence, to:
   H. S. Bennett, Esq., Emmanuel College, Cambridge.
   Professor F. R. H. Du Boulay, Department of History, Bedford College.
   C. P. Davies, Esq., Folkestone Reference Library.
   Dr F. Hull, County Archives, Maidstone.
   J. Kenneth Major, Esq., Reading.
   Miss A. Oakley, Canterbury Cathedral Archives and Library.
   J. Salmon, Esq. Hoxne, Norfolk.
   Dr W. Urry, St Edmund Hall, Oxford.
   Professor Lynn White, Jr., University of California, Los Angeles.

.... and to the staff or members of:
Bourne Hall Library, Ewell, Surrey.
British Museum Map Room, Reading Room, and Newspaper Library.
Department of the Environment.
Kelly's Directories Ltd, Hampton Wick.
Kent Archives Office, Maidstone.
Kent County Planning Department, County Hall, Maidstone.
Kent Local History Societies.
Kent Messenger Group.

Lambeth Palace Library.
Public Record Office.
Science Museum Library.
Society for the Protection of Ancient Buildings.
The author would like to express appreciation to the following photographers whose illustrations are included by permission:
F. J. Ballard (36), Gordon Clemetson (1, 48, 49), E. Hodges (14), Keystone Press (16), J. Styles (20).
All other recent photographs are by Richard West. Numbers 18, 21, 24 are from old postcards, and numbers 4 and 36 are from originals by unknown photographers.
    I would also like to thank my husband not only for his photography but for his interest and support throughout.

Abbreviations:

    N.G.R.   National Grid Reference
    S.P.A.B. The Society for the Protection of Ancient Buildings

J.W.

FOREWORD

Jenny West has a wide knowledge of the windmills of Kent; her accounts are interesting and clear and her illustrations excellent.

As one who was introduced to these mills as long ago as 1925, by the late John Russell of Union Mill, Cranbrook, I have very great pleasure in welcoming the second edition of this book, which deserves a place on the shelves of all who are, or will be, interested in windmills.

Rex Wailes, O.B.E., F.S.A., F.I.MECH.E., F.F.S.A., 1978

INTRODUCTION

Since a comprehensive survey of the windmills of Kent made by William Coles Finch in 1933 (*Watermills and Windmills,* Daniel) there has been a dramatic decrease in their numbers. As in other counties throughout England many have become derelict or have completely disappeared — due in most cases to disuse and the forces of nature, with general lack of finance and in some cases interest, supplementing their loss.

Undoubtedly such loss is unfortunate, for these symbols of a once thriving craft are irreplaceable. Due recognition has, however, been given in recent decades to the necessity for preserving a representative proportion of the county's mills before they too have weakened and fallen; Kent is therefore a county more fortunate than many in retaining some remarkable examples of her windmills, many of which have been recently restored. Such restoration has in no case been easily undertaken but has necessitated considerable finance, and in many instances long periods of negotiation and devoted work on the part of the individuals or bodies concerned. The county is therefore understandably proud of her remaining mills and of the few surviving millers who once worked them — devoted craftsmen who have enabled the accounts of certain mills within this survey to be the richer for the information they have kindly given.

In addition to an account of the Kent windmill scene during seven centuries, interesting features of each existing mill are given, whatever its condition, in addition to its history and plans, if any, for preservation.

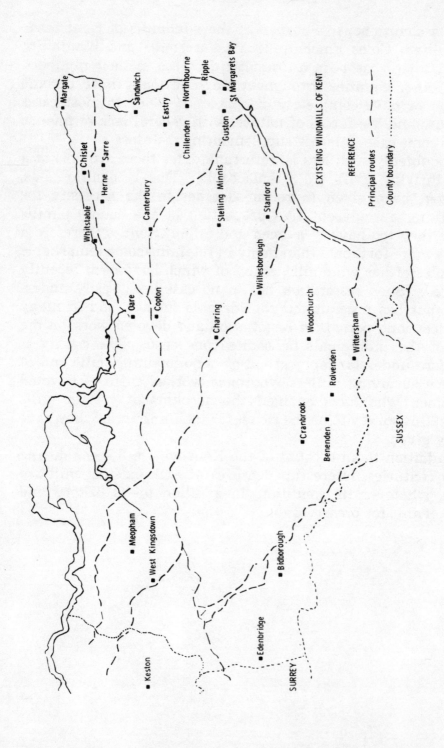

EXISTING WINDMILLS OF KENT

REFERENCE

Principal routes — — —

County boundary ....

Margate

Sandwich

Eastry

Chillenden

Northbourne

Ripple

St Margarets Bay

Guston

Chislet

Herne

Sarre

Whitstable

Canterbury

Stelling Minnis

Stanford

Oare

Copton

Charing

Willesborough

Woodchurch

Wittersham

Rolvenden

Cranbrook

Benenden

SUSSEX

Meopham

West Kingsdown

Bidborough

Edenbridge

Keston

SURREY

KENT'S WINDMILL SCENE — THIRTEENTH CENTURY TO THE PRESENT DAY

*   *   *   *

There are twenty-nine windmills in Kent and the remains of many more. Each has now ceased work and not all are in full mechanical order, but in their widely varied positions along tree-lined lanes, wind-swept cliffs, or majestically dominating a Wealden town, they brave the elements of nature and give valuable evidence of a once thriving industry. One of Britain's most beautiful counties and among her leaders in agriculture, Kent has considerably varied scenery and ways of life, due largely to the variety of her geological outcrops; there is however one feature common to most of her regions — each has at some time during the last seven centuries possessed windmills and the typical life that surrounds them.

The Kent windmill scene has been as colourful and as varied as any. In addition to the traditional four sweep corn mills, the last of which was built at Swingfield in 1885,[1] there have in the past been multi-sweep mills, horizontal mills with their sails or sweeps turning in a horizontal instead of the more usual almost vertical plane, and many employed for purposes other than the milling of corn. Included were mills to separate or grind various seed types — examples having been at Nonington and Birchington; those windmills once concerned in pumping sea water to large evaporating pans in the bygone salt industry in such areas as the Isle of Grain and Richborough; other pumping mills such as those of Oare, Stodmarsh and Iwade used for land drainage, and those of Copton and Margate once employed by the Corporation Water Works; and the last to appear in Kent in 1929, a mill to generate electricity at St Margaret's Bay. Most survivors in this county, however, were erected for the sole purpose of grinding corn.

At various times since the early thirteenth century when the first references were made to windmills in Kent, many hundreds have stood, some on new sites and others assuming the site of a previous mill. The passage of milling has however never run smoothly, Kent being no exception. In the last three centuries alone fire has claimed well over forty mills and heavy gales others; millers, dedicated hard working men in spite of their frequently acclaimed legendary meanness, have faced many hazards and more than a few have been seriously injured or killed at their mills — hit by rotating sweeps or caught by the machinery within. Although, however, the world of milling by wind was one of concentrated work often fraught with danger it was certainly a craft with which all associated were very proud.

Milling was at its height in this county in the first half of the last century, the strength of the wind being harnessed to grind the grain then in abundant supply from the surrounding farmland. With however the introduction of steam power to milling and the formation of large mechanically driven roller mills, the dominance of the windmill in Kent as in other parts of England inevitably passed, and their numbers in the years since have greatly diminished owing to disuse, and in the majority of cases, to the almost inevitable state of disrepair, dereliction and often the demolition which ensues.

With the increasing recognition of their historical importance, both technical and social, combined with the full realisation of their rapidly disappearing numbers, certain private owners of mills, national and local bodies and voluntary organisations have for some time been making every effort to preserve the county's windmills and to restore certain carefully selected examples. (Such work is demonstrated under individual mills in the survey and in the section on Restoration to follow.) Instead therefore of succumbing to the forces of nature many have been able to be preserved as monuments to a vital period in the county's history.

EARLY WINDMILLS OF KENT — THEIR LOCATIONS, DESIGN AND RELATIONSHIP TO THOSE OF OTHER AREAS

Although, as illustrated by the Domesday Survey of 1086, Kent had over three hundred *water* mills, it did not, in common with the remainder of England, have any windmills. Not until over a century later did the windmill .with its invaluable ability to utilize the power of the wind to grind corn make its first appearance in the county.

The first known record of a windmill in Kent refers to one in Little Foxmold in the Ridingate area of Canterbury, on the south-east side of the City. (Little Foxmold being in the area south west of the Old Dover Road, and west of the Ethelbert Road.) The charter concerning the mill, referred to by W. Somner in 1640, but more fully by J. Duncombe and N. Battely in 1785,[2] states that the windmill " Molendinum ad ventum " was granted to the Hospital of Eastbridge by the Prioress and Nuns of the Church of St Sepulchre at a date near 1200 and certainly before 1227. An agreement was apparently made between the above and the master and brothers of the hospital, whereby the latter should hold the said land and windmill, paying annually to the Prioress and Nuns " six pence on Midlent Sunday " with the Nuns bearing a fourth part of the cost of building, repairing and maintaining the mill, while receiving the fourth part of the profits from it and having their own corn ground there free of charge.

Worthy of note in this connection is that a more recent mill — St Laurence smock Mill[3] — is known to have stood on or very near the site of the above mill, its last remains having disappeared at the century's close. How long that first mill stood and how many subsequently replaced it are not known, although it is certain that no mill was recorded at this site on known Kent maps of the period between the sixteenth and nineteenth centuries.

Among other early references are those of a windmill on lands at Terlingham belonging to the Manor of Folkestone in 1263;[4] of one at Dover in 1295;[5] of another at Shorne in 1315, where in a description of the manor of Shorne is noted " 18 acres of land, 3 acres of wood, a meadow and a windmill "[6]; while existing records dating from 1405 give details of such items as the lease and repair of a mill at Herne,[7] and a map of Thanet of 1414 provides evidence of another at the foot of a beacon mound at Birchington.[8]

The windmills of Kent were not the first in England. In neighbouring Surrey is literary evidence of a mill at Warlingham at the close of the twelfth century; in Suffolk of a mill at Dunwich at a date between 1185 and 1199, and one at Bury St Edmunds in 1191; and in Buckinghamshire a mill near Buckingham given in approximately 1189 to Oseney Abbey. The earliest of all known authentic records of English windmills however refers to one known to have been standing by 1185 at Weedley in Yorkshire; while the first available reference to any European windmill concerns one in Normandy in 1180.[9]

The typical design of these mills with their sweeps rotating in an almost vertical plane, and of those subsequently spreading throughout northern and later southern Europe was apparently an invention completely independent of those windmills attributed nearly three centuries earlier to southern Afghanistan and eastern Iran. It is interesting to note that although the typical European design became widespread — even appearing beyond Europe in Syria in 1190 during the Third Crusade, the vertical axle mill of Afghanistan, with its vanes rotating horizontally, was not apparently recorded at any time in any part of Islam west of Eastern Iran.[9] (For later horizontal mills in England see end of Section 1.)

It is unfortunately impossible to estimate with accuracy the number of windmills which stood during the period between the appearance of those first known in the county and what may be considered to be the first complete record of windmills on Symonson's county map of 1596. Mills, whether powered by wind or water, could have been built or destroyed and the former even moved from one site to another without any relevant detail appearing in individual manorial records. Information concerning mill distribution or milling customs within the county is therefore entirely dependent upon chance reference appearing in existing manuscripts of the period.

It is however doubtful whether the restrictive custom of milling soke, then prevalent in many parts of England, by which tenants were compelled to use only the manorial mill to the sole financial gain of the manorial lord, was ever in general use in Kent.[10] Here the custom would almost certainly have been difficult to operate with any efficiency or success due to the more scattered nature of the manorial properties, and the contrasting nature of land tenure. Lands which prior to the Dissolution of the Monasteries were held primarily by religious bodies or individuals or by the Crown were rarely in compact units with a manorial lord in direct personal control of his tenants; they were instead visited only intermittently by distantly residing lords due to their widespread distribution, and were composed of a large proportion of freehold tenants little restricted by manorial custom. Many mills, both wind and water, were in fact by the fifteenth century being leased to millers. The terms of the leases probably varied between one manor and another but frequently stressed that the mill should be kept in repair and production and that the lord's surveyors should be allowed access to inspect it and possibly order repairs.

WINDMILL DISTRIBUTION BETWEEN THE SIXTEENTH AND TWENTIETH CENTURIES

The first complete record of the extant windmills of the county was, as previously mentioned, prepared in 1596 by Philip Symonson, later to become Mayor of Rochester. Valuable knowledge of the distribution of mills of the period may be evolved from this map, in size and detail superior to any English county map of its time. The thirty-nine mills here depicted were clearly concentrated in the fertile corn growing lands of the Isle of Thanet, and in the vicinities of Deal, Sandwich and Romney Marsh; although there was evidence of mills on the Isle of Sheppey and in the lower Medway valley, numbers here were as yet comparatively few.

The subsequent pattern of windmill distribution in the county appears to have been governed to a marked degree by the variation in the main geographical areas, and consequently the number of inhabitants and their typical occupations. As evidenced by the maps of Speed 1610, and of Morden 1680, the mills during the seventeenth century were still concentrated in the fertile wheat growing lands of Thanet and the east coast; included, among others, were those of Margate, Birchington, Sandwich, Deal, Ripple and St Margaret's. In combination with North Kent these areas produced the country's main wheat supply and although it exported large quantities of grain by sea to London, East Anglia and parts of Europe, it had to retain a certain quantity for the requirements of its own growing population. Thus for not only the many agricultural workers of the area but the immigrant cloth workers of Sandwich and the inhabitants of the growing town of Deal and the ports of Dover, Margate and Ramsgate, windmills fulfilled a very definite need and continued to do so for the next two centuries.

Although the Romney and Walland Marsh areas showed seven mills standing during the sixteenth and early seventeenth centuries the number gradually decreased, with only four standing during the last century — at Brenzett, Lydd, Old Romney and Newchurch. This was largely due to the increase in sheep farming on land by now supporting rich pasture — some of which had originally been arable and some reclaimed from the sea. Although previously well populated, the area had, by the seventeenth century, become the most sparsely populated in the county, and with the decrease of both land under wheat and the need for flour the windmill here ceased in its importance.

The three mills of Sheppey in the seventeenth century at Minster, Eastchurch and Elmley must have been quite sufficient for the needs of the sparse population; although the number appears to have fallen in the intervening period it had, by the nineteenth century, risen to five.

For the other main wheat growing areas — North Kent with

two thirds of its land arable, and the chalk slopes of the Downs with over half arable — surprisingly few windmills were depicted on county maps for the sixteenth and seventeenth centuries. As in East Kent, a considerable amount of local wheat was exported to London, although a large proportion must have been milled for the needs of the local population. The North Western region was admittedly well supplied with streams to power water mills and possessed also the windmills of Cobham, Frindsbury, Shorne and Chatham, but it was not until the eighteenth century that Kent maps showed windmills in any significant number in the area immediately east of the lower Medway.

One possible reason for this surprising lack in number was that corn to be milled for local needs could be easily transported via Watling Street to the watermills to the west or those in or near Canterbury, or to the few existing windmills of the area. As depicted by the Ordnance Survey of the early nineteenth century however, windmills were by now concentrated in large numbers along Watling Street and surrounds, featuring most noticeably near Faversham, Rochester, Chatham, Gravesend and Deptford; these localities were requiring increasing quantities of flour for their large port and dockland populations.

The Downs, even at this time of most concentrated milling, although boasting new mills, had few in comparison with North Kent. Almost certainly the main reason for this was the comparatively small local flour requirement due to the previous migration of much of the already low population to the growing industrial areas of the north of the county.

For centuries much of the Weald of Kent had been covered in dense forest supporting few inhabitants, and when in 1596 the county's windmills were depicted upon Symonson's map, the Weald had only two — at Bethersden and Rolvenden. Although the population increased during the following century the windmills did not, for the inhabitants were primarily concerned not with wheat growing but with the cloth industry centred at Cranbrook and the Wealden iron works. With however the clearing of much of the woodland — to provide fuel for cloth dyeing, charcoal in the iron industry, and timber for ship building at Chatham — combined with the later decline in both the iron and cloth industries, farming in the area began to increase. Mixed rather than purely arable farming predominated, but most farmers cultivated corn for their own and livestock requirements. In the succeeding years therefore windmills employed in the grinding of such corn began to

20

appear throughout the Weald, the largest number being in the early nineteenth century.

It was during the period between 1769, when there were approximately ninety-five windmills, and the mid-nineteenth century when there were over two hundred, that milling by wind was at its most active in the county in general — with the exception of Romney Marsh. Most villages at this time continued to be self-sufficient, with one or two mills fulfilling the needs of both inhabitants and their livestock for an entire neighbourhood. Often having in addition an adjoining bake-house with large ovens for breadmaking, the mill was a hive of activity, and apart from the Church, the very core of village life. When the wind proved favourable the miller would work his mill to the full, dealing with both the grain arriving and that awaiting attention from previous windless days. Never for a moment could he relax while the mill was at work — operating the sack hoist, adjusting the stones, replenishing the grain bins above, filling flour sacks below, and above all watching the weather. Upon his expert judgment depended the adjustment of the sweeps, and for the post mill the timely turning to the wind. When the wind lulled he would make minor repairs to structure or machinery, or dress the millstones by cutting accurately the furrows which ground and directed the grain.

On the local mills the farmers were dependent, for to convey corn elsewhere for more competitive milling prices was a procedure not yet generally undertaken. Although principal roads in the county in the eighteenth century were benefiting from the turnpike system of toll-charging to aid maintenance, most routes between village and town were poor, while those between one village and another were virtually non-existent or frequently lost beneath impassable mud.

Gradually however the position in Kent, as in other parts of England, began to change. Windmills continued with their work but the business they had industriously created over a number of centuries was never again to be the same. Although certain mills, such as those of Willesborough, Chillenden and Stanford were not constructed until later in the century, the work of Kent windmills in general had begun to decline some years before this. In the combination of events responsible, one stands above all others — the introduction of steam, and its application to industry. The first large steam mill in the country at Albion Mills, London, had started working in 1784 and was gradually followed by steam flour mills in other parts of the country, thus providing considerable competition for the windmill. As with all mass production prices were less and the millers, who still had to rely on the ways of the wind, found it difficult if not impossible to compete at all.

Competition from large steam mills and the increasing intercommunication of villages and towns was proving adverse enough, but there were further factors involved in this inevitable decline. The production of wheat within the county and therefore the need for local windmills to grind it was becoming markedly less, due to a significant change from arable land to pasture, and the increasing competition from imported wheat. With the movement of large sections of population from country to industrial areas of Kent, much of the farmland previously under wheat changed to pasture with its less demanding labour requirements. In addition the increasing importation of grain from Canada, Australia and the American Middle West created not only overwhelming competition and therefore an adverse effect on local wheat growing, and consequently trade for local windmills, but also resulted in the construction of large steam mills at or near ports; the grain could thus be ground on arrival from abroad by mills which, towards the end of the century, had power driven rollers instead of stones, and distributed throughout the country in the form of readily consumable flour. With comparativly little wheat ever coming its way, and even that so doing coming from local farmers now having a keen eye for competitive milling prices, the windmill's day of unrivalled splendour had unfortunately passed.

In an effort to compete with the large power mills many millers installed various auxiliary plants — steam, suction gas and later oil. These were at first used only when the wind was lacking — the power turning the stones from below; many millers however found it more profitable to continue wholly by auxiliary means.

Although many mills in the county still worked by wind at the beginning of this century, most had by then alternative forms of power installed and were chiefly producing food for livestock. Flour was by now seldom produced in the windmill, for not only was it entirely uneconomical, but it was now more fashionable to consume the white flour of the power mills with their imported grain than the traditional wholemeal flour.

Of over two hundred windmills, known from the Ordnance Survey of 1805-1844 to have been in existence during that period, almost half had disappeared by the time of the

Ordnance Survey of 1903-1910. In 1930 the number had diminished further to seventy, with only fifteen corn mills still working by wind.[1] In the years since, all have ceased work — the last to do so being the mill at Stelling Minnis, in commission until Autumn 1970 — while many of these irreplaceable buildings have entirely disappeared.

Fortunately those which now survive include examples, in varying states of preservation, of the three main types of mill — the post mill with its timber body rotating upon a central post, the timber smock mill, and brick or stone tower mills with fixed towers and revolving caps.

The sails (or, as they are termed in Kent and Sussex, the sweeps) had to face directly into the wind in order to turn, by a system of gearing, the interior milling mechanism and such additional machinery as the sack hoist and the flour dressing machine. For this the body of the post mill carrying its sweeps was turned by hand with the aid of a long tail pole protruding at the rear. Occasionally a cart wheel was fixed to the end of the tail pole and ran along the ground to facilitate turning; as an alternative to turning by hand, the pole could be secured to a horse, or lorry as at Chillenden mill.

Although none survive, the majority of the county's early mills would almost certainly have been of the post type, but without the roundhouse featured by many of the more recent post mills, which enclosed the supporting substructure and provided extra storage space. The oldest surviving in Kent is at Keston; others stand at Rolvenden, Chillenden and Wittersham.

Although the caps of the early smock and tower mills were turned with their sweeps by hand through chain and wheel winding gear, the majority after the mid-eighteenth century were turned automatically by a fantail mechanism. This method, which considerably reduced the work of the miller, as he did not have to adjust the direction of the sweeps manually at every wind change, was occasionally applied to post mills — two in Kent were at Lydd and Wittersham.

Of all mills remaining in Kent the smock with its octagonal-sided tower still predominates — as it did when milling by wind was at its height. The date of construction of the earliest smock mill is not known for certain although among the earliest were those, no longer in existence, constructed in the early part of the eighteenth century. Notable examples standing today are those of Cranbrook, Herne, West Kingsdown, Margate and Meopham.

Of the tower mills remaining, those at Oare, Edenbridge, Stanford and Bidborough are the best but by no means complete. Although Kent tower mills are thought to have been constructed at a slightly later date than smock mills, it is of particular interest that the first known record of a tower mill in England concerns one in this very county — at Dover in 1295. A record of the mill, at Dover Castle, describes the structure as having been of stone, while the site has been identified at the edge of a spur of ground approximately 250 feet south of St Mary's Church.[5]

Unfortunately none remain of the multi-sweep and horizontal types of mill. The county possessed four known multi-sweep mills — a five sweep corn mill at Sandhurst of which only the base now stands; a five sweep pumping mill at Margate; and saw mills at Great Chart and Bethersden, each with six sweeps.

The two known mills with their sweeps revolving in a horizontal plane instead of the usual vertical, at Margate and Sheerness, were, in common with another at Battersea, designed by Captain Stephen Hooper at the end of the eighteenth century.[11]

While the number of windmills in existence has sadly diminished during the last century, the county is indeed fortunate in the number it does possess. It is for this reason that the twenty-nine mills which remain and the part each one played in its respective locality are of particular historical value, not only to all people interested in windmills alone but to all who inhabit, visit or study the county of Kent.

[1] *Watermills and Windmills*, W. Coles Finch. Daniel, 1933.
[2] *Antiquities of Canterbury*, William Somner, 1640. *Bibliotheca Topographica Britannica, XXX. The History and Antiquities of the Three Archiepiscopal Hospitals*, by John Duncombe and Nicholas Battely, 1785. For the site of the mill see *Canterbury under the Angevin Kings*. William Urry. Athlone Press, 1965. Maps 2a, 2b, sheet 9.
[3] Dr W. Urry, personal correspondence.
Watermills and Windmills, W. Coles Finch. Daniel, 1933.
[4] *Archaeological Cantiana*, Volume 3, page 257; Volume 10, page 108.
[5] *A Note on Early Tower Windmills*, John Salmon, B.A. *Journal of the British Archaeological Association, Third Series, Volume XXIX*, 1966, page 75.
[6] *Calendar of Inquisitions Post Mortem*, Edward II. Vol. 6. No. 181.
[7] *Lambeth Court Rolls, No. 80. Treasurer's Accounts of Christ Church Canterbury*, 7-8, Henry IV, 1405-61.
[8] *Map of Thanet by Thomas of Elham*, 1414.
[9] Professor Lynn White, Jr., personal correspondence.
Medieval Technology and Social Change. Lynn White, Jr. Oxford, 1962.
[10] Dr F. Hull, Kent Archives Office, and Miss A. Oakley, Cathedral Archives and Library, Canterbury — personal correspondence.
[11] *Windmills of Surrey and Inner London*, Charles Skilton, 1966. K. G. Farries and M. T. Mason.
I am indebted to Mr A. Allen of Shorne and Mr H. Gough of Herne Bay for informing me of References 6 and 7 respectively.

A SURVEY OF THE EXISTING WINDMILLS
AND MILL REMAINS

*　　　*　　　*　　　*

BENENDEN

Mill position — one mile east of the village centre, on the Cranbrook to Rolvenden route.   N.G.R. TQ 822325

Beacon Mill is the sole survivor of three windmills once standing in the Benenden vicinity; one stood near the existing one on Beacon Hill,[1] while another is thought to have existed at some time to the north east of the present mill, just within the boundary with Biddenden, as evidenced by the names Windmill Hill, Windmill Field, and Mill Bank House on the 1839 Tithe map.[2]

Ending work early this century, the mill had its sweeps removed a few years later and has stood idle ever since. It stands now in poor condition after facing many years of wind and rain in its elevated position; much of the weatherboarding of both smock and cap is falling apart, allowing wind, damp, and numerous birds admittance to the upper floors.

All that remains of the machinery within is the iron wind-shaft, the brake wheel, brake and wallower — all of wood, and a further wooden wheel below, and once in contact with the wallower from which it transmitted the drive for the now bygone sack hoist. Interesting features are the centering rollers for the cap, for these are of wood bonded by metal instead of the more usual all-metal. On the second floor is the great spur wheel of iron with its wooden cogs — all that now signifies the once industrious activity of this stone floor. Of the two-storeyed brick base with part of its first floor timber stage remaining, the upper floor is now used as a store room and the ground floor a garage.

In 1950 the owner of that time had urgent repairs undertaken to make the mill waterproof, although unfortunately no further work was commenced due to a change in ownership of both mill and mill house; the house was sold in 1952 although no purchaser for the mill was forthcoming until 1958. Eventually sold yet again, the mill is now once more owned jointly with the adjacent house.

As with other surviving mills in the county, the date of construction must have been towards the end of the eighteenth, or in the early nineteenth century, for the first known official record of both this and the neighbouring mill was made on maps published in 1821, and for the period 1805-1844.[1]

Millers known to have worked the mill include William Oxley, Richard Reeves, John Barton, Richard Corke, F. Richardson, Thomas Collins Sr. and Jr. and finally Robert Burgess.[3]

Richard Reeves, stated by the 1839 Tithe Map to be the owner of land at and near Beacon Hill, although only the occupier of the mill and house (owner — Spencer Crisford) appears by 1847 to have been in financial difficulties. An existing document states that he decided to sell his property — previously in the ownership of his father Thomas — to three local farmers, to help settle debts. These possessions are stated to have included land known as The Beacon, barns, stables, oasthouses, and other buildings, land totalling fifty-two acres, and a steam corn mill, water engine, and cottages lately erected by Reeves himself. The steam mill must have worked independently of the windmill, for although both were run by Reeves, the windmill is not mentioned here and was therefore presumably on land still owned by the above mentioned Crisford or a successor.[4]

By 1858 a subsequent owner of the windmill, Ebenezer Beeman, was also found to be in debt, as illustrated by a further document. To clear such debts he sold, to one James Golding, the windmill together with " sweeps, sails gear, running tackle and other mill furniture ", half an acre of land formerly part of Beacon Farm, in addition to a stable, dwelling house and waggon lodge;[5] this would have been the property once occupied by Reeves. Such a tragic situation was possibly not infrequently experienced by nineteenth-century millers, competing with an increasing number of large mechanically powered mills.

It is of interest in connection with Benenden windmill that later millers ran it in conjunction with the Mill Street water-mill — Wandle Mill. First recorded as having run both was Thomas Collins, to be followed at his death by his son of the same name — in 1884. It is said locally that the latter hunted and gave champagne parties — living far beyond his income and finally becoming bankrupt — yet another financial tragedy for a Benenden miller. Robert Burgess then ran both mills, from approximately 1899 until 1914 when owner Thomas

Collins died. Although the water mill continued for some time after this, the windmill had by now ground for the last time.

1 *Greenwood's Map of 1821.*
   Ordnance Survey map 1805-1844.
2 *Public Record Office.*
3 *Kelly & Co. Directories 1840-1915.*
   Pigot Directories 1832 and 1834.
4 *Kent Archives Office. U78. T149/4.*
5 *Kent Archives Office. U78. T171.*

BIDBOROUGH

Mill position — north-west of village, on route B.2176 N.G.R. TQ 562435

Bidborough tower mill ended all work at the close of the last century after two sweeps had been damaged in a storm. The remaining exterior machinery was subsequently removed, leaving the tower which stands today.

The exact date of the mill's construction is not known. A mill was depicted on the site on the county map of 1769,[1] while according to Mr Smith, owner of the present mill, reference was made to purchases from the miller of flour for the relief of the poor in the Parish Accounts of 1759, 1763, and in 1765 when the miller was a William Weaver — thus indicating that a mill was standing at least ten years before the first map reference. It cannot however be absolutely certain whether the existing mill was the one to which eighteenth-century reference was made, or one constructed at a later date to replace it. If the original, the mill was of considerably earlier construction than any other existing tower mill — the next being Canterbury, built in the early nineteenth century.

The Tithe Map of 1839[2] names Nicholas Arnold — a miller known to have worked the mill for some years after this date — as owner and occupier of the Windmill, Buildings and Pasture, and of a cottage and garden. Among later millers named in Trade Directories were T. Arnold 1867, Albert Oliver 1891, Oliver and Morris 1895 and finally Joseph Tabraham 1899. Millers for the latter two dates appear to have also run a water mill near Speldhurst.

Although there was apparently speculation in 1933 regarding the possible restoration of the mill, plans by the owner at that period obviously did not materialise, for no visible attempt was made at improving or preserving the structure. In 1942 the cap and its entire contents were blown from the tower during a storm — the windshaft, according to Mr Smith, becoming partially embedded in the ground due to its own immense weight. A similarly shaped cap was constructed in 1949 although this in turn needed replacement recently, by a flat roof, when the outer walls of the mill were plastered.

Nothing remains on the stone, bin or dust floors but all machinery on the first or meal floor is intact. Fortunately the three stones were underdriven so that the great spur wheel, of cast iron with wooden cogs, is still in existence at this level. To the spur wheel, through a system of gearing from a wheel on the mill's exterior, ran the auxiliary power supplied by a tractor below. Suspended in front of the spur wheel is a wooden shield which would have prevented grain-filled sacks from swinging against moving machinery as they made their way up the mill by sack hoist. The shield's lower edge has obviously been well worn by this function.

The ground floor now houses a power-driven hammer mill, working entirely independently of the machinery above; here grain is ground to produce meal for the dairy herd on the surrounding land. The hayfield visible on a photograph taken at the turn of the century disappeared many years ago but has been replaced by the equally delightful scene of Mr Smith's private residence and perfectly tended country garden. Just visible through shrubs and trees is the original miller's cottage, mentioned on the Tithe Map.

From both the mill and the grounds which surround it, is one of the most magnificent views in the county: beyond acre upon acre of the undulating farmland which once supplied the mill with corn, the fertile Weald stretches on into Sussex.

[1] *Map of Kent by J. Andrews, A Drury and W. Herbert. 1769.*
[2] *Public Record Office.*

CANTERBURY

Mill position — Windmill Close, St Martins Hill. N.G.R. TR 161578

St Martin's Mill is the sole survivor of six windmills known to have stood in the vicinity during the last two centuries — one having been almost opposite on St Martin's Hill until 1868. Since ending work at the end of the last century it has functioned in various capacities, and although now a private residence, has, in addition to serving as an observation tower in wartime, acted as a guest house and honeymoon retreat.

The mill, which has the original miller's house standing nearby in Windmill Close, was built in 1817. Unfortunately, as with other existing mills which went out of commission at the turn of the century, there appears to be comparatively little information available on its working life.

The Tithe Map of the St Martin's area of Canterbury of 1839[1] shows that the mill and garden, which are drawn in detail, were owned by Elizabeth Adams — almost certainly a relative of John Adams for whom the mill was built — and occupied by Thomas Marsh, who is said to have later milled at Cranbrook and Sissinghurst.[2] On the north, east and west sides of the mill was Mill Field which was arable land worked by a John Collard, while on the opposite side of the road near a turnpike was a " mill garden "; although not specifically including a mill this must have been the location of the mill which disappeared later in the century, for the occupier was Samuel Beard — depicted in a later directory as miller.

Millers subsequently associated with the St Martin's Hill milling business, traced from various Canterbury directories, include the names of Gooderson, Richardson, Bradley, Robinson, Bax, Coaks, Rackham and Lawrence.[3] Presumably where two millers were named for 1859 and 1867, one worked the now bygone mill opposite. In addition, it would appear that the mention of " steam mill " against the name of Gooderson in 1859 referred to either auxiliary power or a separate steam plant connected with business at the present mill, for when the term " steam and windmill " is applied later in 1882 and 1889, the mill opposite had already disappeared.

In 1920 a Canterbury builder, Mr Cozens, bought and considerably renovated the (by now unworked) mill, used the millstones for garden decoration and built the large house now adjacent. The late owner, Mr Butterfield, recently quoted one rather amusing incident involving both Mr Cozens and the mill; on assuming ownership the latter had a powerful telescope installed inside the cap, and although not intending the instrument for such a purpose, he happened one day to observe with its aid some of his workmen idling on a building site. He subsequently lowered their wages accordingly that week!

After the last war the mill and adjacent house had several changes of ownership, becoming first a guest house, with the honeymoon room on an upper floor of the mill, and then a restaurant. The restaurant was later closed and the house — at times said to be haunted — used as a private dwelling. Although in 1958 there was a possibility that the structure might be demolished, a Building Preservation Order was imposed by the then Ministry of Housing and Local Government, and the possible action evaded.

The mill tower, which was thus enabled to survive, has retained its timber cap — the only mill of this type in the county to do so. Visible are the sweep middlings, fan stage, and a louvred extension on the top of the cap adapted during the war when the mill was used as an observation post. Sweeps and fantail are missing. Within the cap remains the cast iron windshaft, and the brake wheel, once driving via the wallower three pairs of stones. A sack hoist once present was powered by friction from the under rim of the wallower.

It is interesting to note that the first windmill to be recorded in Canterbury was, as mentioned in Section I, already standing by the beginning of the thirteenth century, in the Ridingate area on the south-east side of the city.

1 *Public Record Office.*
2 *Folkestone Herald, March 1933.*
3 *Canterbury Directories, 1859-1900. Public Library, Canterbury.*

CHARING

Mill position — on the brow of Charing Hill, half mile west of route A.252. N.G.R. TQ 957503.

Unfortunately Charing Hill Mill has retained little internal machinery, has lost sweeps and fantail, and lacks the detailed information of past milling days available for many other Kent mills. This is however to some extent compensated for by the mill's magnificent position high on the North Downs to the north west of Ashford.

Standing above Charing village, the site of a mediaeval manor once held by the Archbishop of Canterbury, this tarred smock mill with its distinctive white cap and first floor staging is in the private grounds of the Mill House. The house, which has been befittingly extended to form a large attractive residence among secluded terraced gardens, shares with the mill views over undulating pasture and woodland on the south west slope of the Downs. Just below the mill grounds is the Pilgrims' Way, followed during the Middle Ages by many hundreds of pilgrims travelling to the shrine of St Thomas Becket at Canterbury.

In assuming the role of studio, billiard room, and even quarters for pet rabbits at various times during the early part of this century, it is not surprising that the mill had much of its machinery removed below the cap. The brake wheel with its wooden brake, the cast iron windshaft, and the cap winding gear allowing manual operation from within are present, while below on the third floor are the wooden wallower and the sack hoist which operated from it. The wooden great spur wheel is fortunately still in existence although the stones to which it once transmitted power are not. No other machinery is present. The sweeps — two common and two spring — were removed early this century after being considered dangerous.

The mill structure is in good condition, having recently been repaired by millwrights Messrs Vincent Pargeter and Philip Lennard. In April 1970 they reframed and re-boarded the head and tail gables of the cap, replaced some of the weatherboarding and framing of the mill body and refaced one of the cant posts for approximately eight feet.

The first county maps on which the mill is depicted are those of Greenwood of 1821 and the 1805-44 Ordnance Survey map. It was not included in Hasted's survey undertaken for his maps published between 1778 and 1801, so must therefore have been constructed towards the end of the eighteenth, or in the early nineteenth century.

Although previously described as Field Mill,[1] the 1839 Charing Tithe Map clearly bestows this title on the water mill near Egerton, just within the western boundary of Charing Parish;[2] this states that " Field Mill, House and Buildings " were owned by Earl Cornwallis and occupied by Horace Bates. The windmill however, shown at its present site on Charing Hill, is depicted as " House, Windmill and Garden " and the owner and occupier as Richard Chapman Jennings, who also owned arable and pasture land near the village centre.

The miller between approximately 1823 and 1827 is known to have been Thomas Parks, " baker and miller ", while later in the century the above mentioned Richard Jennings was replaced by A. Sidders; subsequent millers included S.

Andrews, William Smith, and in 1887 George Smith, described as miller " at the wind and water mills ".[3]

The last miller here was Walter Hicks who later left to work the above mentioned water mill — Field Mill; there he was aided by his son Henry (see Cranbrook Mill) — the two later moving to the smock mill at Smarden. Charing windmill ended all work in 1891, and it was at that date that Walter Hicks was preparing to transfer his interests to Field Mill. In existence are both a Tenancy Agreement between " Walter Hicks of Charing Mill, and Fiennes Stanley Wykeham Cornwallis Esq. M.P. of Linton Park, Maidstone ", concerning the yearly tenancy of " Field Mill and Farm, Charing " at £60 rent, and an agreement concerning the subsequent lease of this water mill in 1893 for twenty-one years to the same miller.[4]

Of interest in connection with the mills of Charing is that a second windmill appears to have once stood on Charing Heath, in the vicinity of Field Mill, for a windmill is illustrated near the Windmill Inn on the Ordnance Survey map of 1903. The site is only marked by the words " Wind hill " on previous Ordnance Survey maps. It is possible that the miller George Smith of " wind and water mills " worked this and not the present mill.

[1] *Watermills and Windmills, W. Coles Finch. Daniel. 1933.*
[2] *Public Record Office.*
[3] *Pigot's Directories 1823-4 and 1826-7.*
   Kelly & Co. Directories 1847-87.
[4] *Kent Archives Office, U24 T320.*

CHILLENDEN

Position — on farmland directly north of the village. N.G.R. TR 268543

No windmill could fit more perfectly into the neighbouring countryside than the post mill at Chillenden. Standing open to the changing winds, it looks over undulating corn fields and country lanes, to the coast several miles distant on one side and the village of Chillenden on the other. Owned until 1958 by Brigadier Speed, the mill was then acquired by the County Council, subsequently undergoing certain restoration.

This is one of Kent's four complete post mills to remain. Although of the open trestle type with post, supporting quarter-

1. Cranbrook Mill

2. Benenden Mill

4. Bidborough Mill

3. Benenden Mill in working order

5. Bidborough Mill, at turn of century

6. Canterbury Mill

7. Charing Mill

8. Chillenden Mill

9. Chislet Mill

11. Eastry Mill

10. Chislet Mill, early this century

12. Edenbridge Mill

13. Guston Mill

14. Guston Mill, working condition pre-1940

15. Herne Mill

16. West Kingsdown Mill,
undergoing restoration

17. West Kingsdown Mill

18. Keston Mill

19. Margate Mill, pre-1927

20. Margate Mill, looking into the cap from dust floor, 1974

21. Margate Mill,
working by engine, 1931

22. Margate Mill, 1978

23. Meopham Mill

24. Northbourne Mill,
working order 1913

25. Northbourne Mill

26. Oare Mill

27. Ripple Mill, in working order

28. Ripple Mill

29. Rolvenden Mill

30. St. Margaret's Bay Mill

31. Sandwich Mill

32. Sandwich Mill, 1978

33. Sarre Mill

34. Sarre Mill in working order, 1908

35. Stanford Mill

36. Stanford Mill, working order pre-1950

37. Stelling Minnis Mill, 1937

38. Stelling Minnis Mill after restoration, 1978

39. Whitstable Mill

40. Willesborough Mill

41. Willesborough Mill in working order in the 1930s

42. Wittersham Mill

43. Woodchurch Mill

44. Woodchurch Lower Mill early this century. Upper Mill in background

45. Drainage Mill near Stodmarsh

46. Copton Pumping Mill

47. Iwade Drainage Mill

48. Lifting runner stone for dressing: Mr J. Russell, Cranbrook Mill

49. Stone dressing: Mr Hicks at Cranbrook Mill

bars and cross-trees exposed to the elements, the mill is not as old as might be expected; apparently replacing an earlier post mill, as evidenced by seventeenth-to nineteenth-century county maps, it was constructed as recently as 1868. It thus became not only the youngest post mill but one of the most recent of any type in Kent.

Although many years have passed since the grinding of wheat for flour, the mill continued grinding grain for livestock until 1949. Mr N. W. Laker worked the mill until that date, succeeding his uncle Mr A. Laker with whom he had worked for many years. A considerable amount of grain was put through the mill in the first year of the last war, but Mr Laker states that the trade was subsequently confronted by the increase in the alternative means of milling created by the powered machines owned by individual farmers.

Although a recently constructed post mill it had no fantail. It had therefore always been turned manually to the wind by its long white tail pole, guided in its revolution by the cart-wheel on which it rests. Aid for this was successfully sought in the form of a lorry attached to the pole; when the mill had to follow a fickle wind the lorry came to the fore.

Mr Laker, aged only thirty-one when he left the mill and therefore one of Kent's youngest ex-windmillers, knew well the changing face of the wind and how best to use it. In assessing the direction of that vital force on which his livelihood depended he would stand at the rear of the mill; if aware, by the wind on his face, of a change to one side or the other he would turn the mill accordingly. Having set the spring sweeps with their canvas-covered shutters, he would run the mill to the full. He well remembers the characteristic sway, not only of the timber body performing its essential task, but of the steps behind rocking to and fro in the grass in accordance; there was nothing like a good east wind! If the mill should get too fast he would move it just out of the wind's full force before applying the brake — thus reducing the possibility of fire from the friction of the brake on the brake wheel. The mill remained thus in full swing until 1949 when a gale felled one of its sweeps.

It is certainly difficult in this day of the large mechanically powered mill to imagine how a miller ever coped with the complex responsibilities of a post mill. Checking the supply of grain to the stones, dressing the flour, noticing any change in the wind, turning the mill, setting the spring or common sweeps, and in Mr Laker's case performing his own stone dressing and operating a separate adjoining oil plant — all now seems quite incredible.

After it ceased to function, the mill with its three remaining sweeps suffered further deterioration — a cause for considerable concern to the Wind and Watermill Section of the S.P.A.B. and the Committee for the Preservation of Rural Kent. In 1950 the Section arranged for initial reports to be made on the mill structure prior to advising on possible future restoration. After receiving a report by its Technical Adviser, and a millwright's estimate for the cost of repair, the Section suggested the possibility of the initiation of a local fund-raising appeal.

Local inhabitants succeeded in raising enough for the mill to be made weatherproof in 1955, but not for full repair. In a revised report of the mill's condition made in the previous year it had been found that due to further deterioration in the intervening years, the repair necessary had extended to include the renewal of tail pole, steps and brick piers supporting the cross trees, in addition to the repair of three sweeps and the renewal of the fourth and much of the mill weatherboarding. It was however finally decided by the Kent County Council in 1958 that to avoid even further deterioration of the structure, it should itself acquire the mill and finance the restoration, now so essential to future existence — the cost of maintenance thereafter to be aided, as previously planned, by the Eastry Rural District Council.

Restoration was subsequently undertaken, but while undoubtedly the mill is one of the more fortunate of those in the county in having received such repair, it is nevertheless unfortunate that while so much work was undertaken on the actual structure, certain milling equipment within was entirely removed. Such equipment included stone tuns and hoppers, a flour dresser, many of the meal chutes and the maize kibbler. All other machinery is present.

The sack hoist was operated by a chain, driven by a pulley on the windshaft behind the brake wheel. The latter, with its fifty wooden cogs, drove the two pairs of underdriven stones indirectly by the cast iron wallower with which it engaged and the iron great spur wheel. The two centrifugal governors are complete. Apart from an additional geared ring on the lower face of the great spur wheel which suffered injury when engagement with the maize kibbler was attempted while in full motion, the machinery present is in good order.

Millers preceding the Laker family at Chillenden were Messrs Haywood and Cage, "millers and farmers", and William Hopper Bean.[1]

[1] *Kelly & Co. Directories 1882-99.*

CHISLET

Mill position — in Brook Road, half mile north west of route A.299. Two miles north of Chislet village. N.G.R. TR 224679.

One of Kent's oldest remaining windmills, with much of its interior machinery of wood instead of the combination of wood and iron characteristic of most later mills, the smock mill at Chislet appears to have been run initially by the family of May in the mid-eighteenth century. On a beam near the ground floor entrance is a carved plaque bearing the inscriptions —
" Anthony May 1765. A. May 1789. M. May 1795."
If, in view of the first date, the mill was already in existence, it would appear that the survey of this area in preparation for the first large scale map of Kent of 1769 must already have been completed by the time the mill appeared for it was not depicted upon it. It does, however, appear on a coastal map of 1774,[1] and later on Greenwood's Map of 1820.

Henry Collard was miller in 1847, while some years later the miller was a Jonathan Packer — later known to have run the nearby mill at Hoath — and the owner of the mill another member of the Collard family — Edwin. In 1878 the mill was taken over by Mr John Wootton; for a time he was joined by his brother Thomas, who later left to purchase Herne Mill. The former, then joined by his son John Walter, ran the mill until his death in 1918.[2] For the two years preceding this and for a few years after the First World War the power for all milling was a paraffin engine; during the war the structure was used as an aircraft observation post.

John Walter Wootton himself replaced two cant posts and installed a new pair of stones while continuing to work the mill; when the business eventually ended he joined his brother Henry in farming over two hundred acres at Marshside Farm near Chislet village.

The sudden cessation of milling by wind in 1916 was entirely due to the mill being tail-winded — a not uncommon tragedy in the milling world — but in this case having an unusual cause. According to the above Henry Wootton, born at the Mill House a number of years before the happening, the sound of the revolving fantail became intolerable one night for the man at that time renting the Mill House; on deciding that action must be taken the tenant purposely disrupted the mechanism by tying the fantail to its staging. The cap and sweeps, no longer turned into the changing wind, were torn from the mill, never to work again.

The mill is now owned privately by Mr Springham who lives in the adjacent Old Mill House. A possible cause for controversy has been the corrugated sheeting in which the smock was encased shortly before milling ended; certainly the mill does not now compare externally with certain well-preserved or restored examples in the county, but it cannot be denied that while many Kent windmills have fallen, this old mill at Chislet has survived — its framework and interior protected by the covering from coastal winds.

Although parts of the flooring, particularly the first or stone floor, are rotting in places, the interior machinery is in good condition. The top or dust floor retains its wooden wallower and the sack hoist, and from the window at this level is an impressive view of farmland stretching to Reculver and the coast. The partitioned wooden bins, once storing grain ready for milling on the floor below, are present on the second floor, while on the first are three pairs of stones — two with tuns — once powered from below. The great spur wheel and two of the three pairs of stone nuts on the ground floor are composed entirely of wood, while the third stone nut is all metal — probably a later replacement. The three governors and a flour dressing machine also remain.

1 *Map for Trinity House by Murdoch McKenzie Jr., 1774.*
2 *Kelly & Co. Directories 1840-1899. Map Room, British Museum. Bagshaw's Directory 1847.*

CRANBROOK

Mill position — The Hill, within the town centre.   N.G.R. TQ 779359.

Whenever reference is made to Union Mill, Cranbrook, it is described as one of the most impressive in the country. This it most certainly is. Majestically dominating the surrounding

Wealden market town once famous for its iron-smelting and cloth-making, this white smock mill with its three storeyed black base rises over seventy feet above ground level.

Constructed in 1814 for Henry Dobell, the mill is the sole survivor of several once in the vicinity[1] and of others in the county known to have been constructed by the same millwright — Humphrey. It was originally built with common sweeps and no fantail, the cap being hand-turned by a chain and wheel winding gear by manipulating an endless chain from outside. Still present at the side of the cap is the large winding wheel once concerned with this. The mill was however modernised in 1840 when George Warren of Hawkhurst added the fantail mechanism to turn the sweeps to the wind, and Medhurst, the Lewes millwright, fitted a new windshaft and patent sweeps.

For fifty years the three pairs of stones, of which two remain, were powered by wind alone. To supplement the wind's varying forces however, auxiliary power was commenced in approximately 1863 in the form of a steam engine, which together with extra stones was brought from a Smarden steam mill.[2] This was superseded in 1919 by a suction gas plant and in 1954 by an independent electric motor, the power in use today. Although the milling of flour ceased here many years ago, the only grain now entering being prepared for livestock, the mill is in full mechanical order.

That it stands now as when originally constructed, with certain later modernizations, has been made possible by three major factors — the careful maintenance afforded for many years by its late owner and miller Mr John Russell, the mill's restoration completed in 1960, and the attention given in the years to follow by miller Mr Henry Hicks.

Mr Russell, by whose family the mill had been owned since 1832, was the first miller to be awarded a Certificate by the Windmill Section of the S.P.A.B. for "zeal shown in the maintenance of his mill", and with the continued encouragement of the Section he continued to undertake necessary repairs, including the renewal of fantail and sweeps, in addition to running the mill. When however by 1950 he was unable to continue with the former arduous task, and unable personally to finance the employment of a professional millwright, it was realised by the Section and Local and County Authorities that an alternative arrangement would be necessary to ensure the future preservation of this famous landmark.

A report by Mr Rex Wailes, Honorary Technical Adviser to the Wind and Watermill Section, was made to assess the degree of repair necessary to the mill, followed by an estimate by the Dutch millwright Mr C. Bremer; after considerable further negotiation the Section, with the support of National and County Authorities and Organisations, launched a national fund-raising appeal. The mill was, with the consent of the Ministry of Housing and Local Government, acquired in 1957 by the County Council — subsequently to be leased back for milling purposes. Although the results of the appeal and the financial help to be given by the Historic Buildings Council, Kent County Council and Cranbrook Rural District Council were not yet sufficient to cover the full cost of restoration, initial stages of the operation were commenced by the Dutch firm in 1958 — on the day that Mr Russell died.

The first of two steel middlings, transported from Holland, and appropriately draped with the British and Dutch flags for the occasion, was triumphantly erected later in the year in the presence of members of the Wind and Watermill Section; the second was installed a week later. Due however to the need for more extensive repair, discovered when the boarding was removed, together with lack of immediately forthcoming finance, and the need for the millwrights to fulfil previously arranged commitments back in Holland, no further work was undertaken until 1960. To enable the restoration to be completed the County Council underwrote the outstanding figure, and at a combined total cost of £6000 this considerable operation — which had included the renewal of sweeps, weatherboarding of the cap and much of the smock, the renewal or splicing of several cant and supporting posts, and the repair of the curb — was completed.

Union Mill was officially re-opened, in the presence of representatives of the National, County and Local bodies which had supported restoration, by Mr Rex Wailes who, on behalf of the Wind and Watermill Section, had supervised the entire undertaking. The sweeps were then set in motion for the first time for six years.

This was in addition a particularly important day for the above-mentioned Mr Henry Hicks, an experienced miller who had joined the Cranbrook team in 1948. Originally from East Mill, Smarden, the late Mr Hicks played an important role in the closing years of milling by wind at Union Mill, and although by this time most of the grain was ground by gas power, he occasionally milled barley by wind during his early years here. Although many of his working days were at mills since gone, he gave invaluable time, energy and experience to this mill, and until his comparatively recent retirement under-took the regular greasing of the curb and fan gearing and the turning of the sweeps through ninety degrees.

Originating from a truly milling family — a great-grand-father at Mayfield watermill, Sussex; a great-uncle at Withering Den mill, and his own father, the last man to work Charing mill — he soon acquired essential highly skilled techniques. Among these were the art of forming composition stones of liquid salt, magnesium cement and emery grit, and that of dressing both these and Peak stones. The continual dressing of the stones left its characteristic mark on Mr Hicks; small grey-blue streaks on the back of his left hand, caused by the flying splinters of steel from his mill bill.

His childhood and early working years were spent with his father, Walter Hicks, at Charing Watermill, near Egerton (see Charing mill). In conjunction with this they ran a grain store near Pluckley Station. When they eventually took possession of Smarden smock mill in 1920 Henry Hicks was twenty-one years old. Unfortunately he worked there for only three years before the structure was tail-winded and put out of commission. Milling was then transferred to oil and later electric powered machinery in a separate building and there Mr Hicks had since been busily engaged until moving to Cranbrook.

1 *Watermills and Windmills of Cranbrook*, *C.C.R.Pile. Cranbrook & Sissinghurst Local History Society, 1954.*
2 *Mr Henry Hicks, personal correspondence.*

EASTRY

Mill position — adjoining the mill house — 'Tewkesbury' in Mill Lane. N.G.R. TR 304545.

Since Symonson depicted a windmill at Eastry on his map of 1596, all county maps except that of Speed in 1610 have recorded one or more mills in the vicinity. In all, six different mills are thus shown to have stood at various times since the sixteenth century; the first disappeared but was replaced by another by 1680,[1] which in turn was joined by one to the north-east in 1736,[2] and by three more nearby at the beginning of the last century. Only one of the group of four once in close proximity is now in existence — the last of the others, at Nurseries to the rear, having disappeared earlier this century.

One of the last men to work the machinery of the present mill was Mr H. Clark (by whose family the mill had been owned since 1826, the first member having been Thomas Clark).[3] He used not wind, but a gas engine for all milling power, the sweeps having already been dismantled, and had the first floor staging covered below to form a roof over the power house and grain store. The mill, once closely surrounded by fields which have in part now made way for houses, was taken over on the retirement of Mr Clark in 1949 by his son Arthur who employed only electric motors for grinding and mixing animal foods. In 1959 he transferred the entire milling business to a vacant brewery in Sandwich renaming it " Guestling Mill ".

Thought to be over two hundred years old, Eastry mill is now devoid of all machinery except the cast iron windshaft, the wooden brake wheel, now without cogs, and the metal brake. The wallower which has gone was possibly removed earlier this century at the same time as the sweeps and fantail. At present the cap, which leans precariously forward due to weakening of the timber ribs, has loose weatherboarding, and with certain parts missing is admitting strong winds and rain over the remaining machinery.

The second floor, below the grain storage bins, has lost its stones and at this level much of the weatherboarding and inner matchboarding has rotted, allowing rain to enter and in turn cause deterioration to certain cant and supporting posts. The first or meal floor marks the transition from brick base to timber smock and here the floor is rotting badly in places. The walls at this level retain much of the white plastering applied at some time in the mill's career, while to one side is the miller's desk now at rest after many busy years.

Remembering two mills at work in the early part of this century is Mr Kemp, one of Eastry's oldest residents. Now aged over eighty years, he recalls the work he undertook for a number of years for the Clark family, starting in 1913 under Mr W. Clark. The sweeps of the mill had disappeared by his arrival, the milling machinery used for the production of animal feed being worked, as later, by a suction gas engine, and a roller plant being run independently to produce flour. Apart from helping in the mill, Mr Kemp's weekly duties consisted of four days on the " rounds " with a one-horse waggon, stabled with a two-horse waggon and ponies to the rear of the mill. Rounds, which sometimes entailed travelling as far as Adisham, included the delivery, within the vicinity, of meal for livestock,

40

flour, and also bread baked by another member of the Clark family in an adjacent bakehouse. He drove also to local farms to collect various grains for milling, and to Sandwich for imported wheat which had been conveyed by rail or water from one of the coastal ports. Mr Kemp states that the latter would be mixed at the mill with English wheat to produce the desired consistency of flour — entirely home-grown wheat of those days giving " sticky " flour which was unsuitable for bread making.

Deliveries were made in addition for the other mill, once approximately a hundred yards behind, also under the Clark family and then still run by wind. It was in fact while collecting meal for loading from that particular mill that Mr Kemp experienced possibly one of the luckiest escapes by anyone ever associated with milling. Although the sweeps were motionless on his arrival, they suddenly started to rotate as the horse and waggon approached the mill entrance; the miller within, totally unaware of his colleague's presence, had freed the brake to enable the day's milling to commence. Before the waggon could be moved it was struck and considerably damaged by one of the sweeps; miraculously however neither man nor horse received injury.

Permission to have the mill demolished was recently sought from the County Council by the present owners Mr and Mrs G. W. Hicks, when they felt that the structure might be unsafe. A structural report was made by the Honorary Millwright to the Wind and Watermill Section of the S.P.A.B. for the County Council Planning Department; it was found that although requiring considerable repair in order to preserve it and prevent possible hazard from further deterioration, the mill was not thought to be of immediate serious danger to the neighbourhood. Permission for demolition of the mill was consequently refused.

1 Morden's map of 1680. Kent Archives Office.
2 Bowen's map of 1736.
3 Pigot and Co: Commercial Directory, 1826-27.

EDENBRIDGE

Mill position — in the grounds of Windmill House; next to the Hospital on the west side of route B.2026. N.G.R. TQ 444457.

The tower mill standing to the south of Edenbridge and the

River Eden has been entirely idle during the present century and is now devoid of all exterior and most interior machinery.

The sweeps, and later the fantail of this mill — built early last century — were removed after milling ceased in approximately 1887; the cap, reported to be deteriorating badly in 1937,[1] eventually shared the same fate, to be subsequently replaced by the present flat boarded roof. The domed cap was a feature shared by only three other known Kent mills — Plumstead, Cobham, and one near Rochester; this was in contrast to the more usual caps of Kent's smock and tower mills, shaped like the roof of a post mill.

Although suggestions were made at the above date to the owner, by the Windmill Section of the S.P.A.B., concerning the possibility of local support for financing the repair and future preservation of the mill, such support was not forthcoming; no repair was therefore undertaken. The owner however fortunately resisted the temptation to have the entire mill demolished, thus enabling the structure to continue in its position of prominence in the attractive gardens of Windmill House.

Within the tower lie the wallower, now out of position on the flooring of the fourth or top floor, and nearby five vanes from the fantail once turning cap and sweeps to the wind. The grain bins remain, while below on the second floor is the iron great spur wheel, now without cogs, which once conveyed power to the overdriven stones; the latter are unfortunately no longer in existence. First and second floors are devoid of all original contents and now act only for private storage purposes.

Although as at certain other Kent mills first-hand information on the daily running of the milling business is lacking due to absence of any surviving miller, there are fortunately in existence certain valuable details of repair of the machinery of this mill, undertaken in the early nineteenth century. These are found in two accounts ledgers of Westerham millwright William Ashby,[2] who worked on many wind and water mills in North East Surrey and West Kent. The ledgers concern work undertaken by Ashby with the help of several sons, between 1825 and 1839, on both Edenbridge windmill — owned by Robert Parsons and run by Edward Bridger — and the nearby watermill owned and run by James and Frederick Stanford respectively.

In 1825 Ashby records the accounts for work done for Parsons on certain farm machinery and later repair and replacements for the mill starting on October 13th as follows:

	£	s	d
1825, 10m' (i.e. October) 13th			
A stop brass for connecting rod of sails	1	6	6
Drilling six holes in 2 brasses.		1	0
22nd. 5 cogs for the brake wheel		4	2
27th. A new neck brass for windshaft			
2 brasses for upright shaft	1	10	6
Drilling 4 screw holes in brass			6
Iron carriage for windshaft neck brass	2	10	6
Fitting neck brass into iron carriage.			
2 men, — 3 days, and 2 men — 1½ days	1	16	6
Self — 2 days		9	0

Just three months later, on January 21st, Ashby was asked by Parsons to value the mill gear and machinery, an undertaking for which the amount of £3.3.0 was charged. This is followed by further interesting details of the millwright's craft and the charge, as before, where clearly legible.

	£	s	d
1826. 9m' (September) 6th.			
Self to look at Midlen (middling),			
20 short vanes. 2 coats of paint.	3	15	0
6 long vanes. 2 coats of paint.			
Tentering and drilling, 21 Thrimbels.		5	0
30th. 6 new sail bars. 9ft. long at 2/2.		13	0
1 man, — 1 day and ¼ day.		5	3
Son — 1 day and ¼ day.		5	3
1827. 11m'.			
32 cogs at 6'.		16	0
26 cogs at 7'		15	2
Self 1½ days.		6	9
1828. 9m'. 5th.			
6 cogs. Dressing tackle, 2 sheets 28 wire		—	—
1831. 7m'. 5th			
2 new brasses for top Baren (Bearing) of upright shaft.		—	—

From the Edenbridge Tithe Map of 1844,[3] it is evident that the above-mentioned Robert Parsons, earlier described as " miller and maltster ", was at this date still the owner of the mill. He owned in addition, the Mill House and other buildings, the nearby millfield of pasture, a malthouse and hop fields. It is not clear from the Tithe records whether he now worked the mill alone, or employed an assistant as earlier. Signifying the probable presence of a fellow-miller is the pencilled inscription of "H. Sisley, 1844" on the meal bin within the mill.

Also inscribed are the faded names of "James ? 1849" — possibly James Mellish, a subsequent miller, and "Stanford 1854". Although for many years the Stanford family ran only the nearby watermill it later acquired the windmill also and for a while ran the two at the same time. The exact date of this acquisition however is not certain. Millers at the windmill in the second half of the century included Moses Brooks, described as miller and coal merchant, who worked the mill for approximately ten years until 1874; and the above-mentioned James Mellish and Son, miller, baker and corn dealer. Mellish would appear to have been employed by the Stanford family at both wind *and* watermills at various periods, for although milling at one or other mill continually for approximately forty years until the windmill went out of commission in 1887, his place at the windmill was, for an intervening period, clearly taken by Moses Brooks.[4] No miller is named for the windmill in any Directory after 1887.

(J. Bassett, mentioned as a miller on both the 1841 Census and Tithe Map, is thought to have run only the watermill to the south-west of the village — Christmas Mill, and not the windmill.)

[1] *Report to the Windmill Section of the S.P.A.B.*
[2] *Kent Archives Office. QCI 1/1 and 1/2.*
[3] *Public Record Office.*
[4] *Kelly & Co. Directories 1847-1887.*

GUSTON

Mill position — approximately three quarters mile east of Guston, in country lane off route A.258.   N.G.R. TR 334444.

The capless brick tower of Swingate Mill at Guston has been idle for many years, and now has a completely different and somewhat unusual function. Part of the ground floor is used by the mill owner Miss Tomsett as a cats' boarding home, while the first floor, though rotting in parts, is used as a nesting sanctuary for doves, which enter at leisure through an open window.

Most of the timber flooring above first floor level is rotting badly and unfortunately prevents any safe possibility of investigating the presence of machinery, other than the flour dressing machine on the " dove " floor, which prepared the flour milled in abundance during the last century. It is however known that although when tail-winded in 1959 the mill lost its cap, fan-staging and last pair of sweeps, it then still retained all interior machinery, including three pairs of stones.

The mill was constructed in the mid-nineteenth century and run until 1907 by John Mummery, followed in that year by Ebenezer Mummery.[1] Although run, after the First World War, by a Mr Sheaff, the mill was by 1930 idle and up for sale. It was after this that the late Mr Tomsett, father of the present owner, bought the mill and worked it by wind until approximately 1943.

Miss Tomsett helped her father regularly in the milling years of the 1930's preparing not flour, but grain for livestock. On one occasion while the latter was harvesting nearby, Miss Tomsett noticed smoke issuing forth from between the stones, for a bolt had entered the hopper from the grain bins above. The mill had to be stopped before the runner stone could be lifted to free the offending object which had mistakenly entered a sack of grain from the adjacent farmland. One happier occasion at the mill was in 1936 at the time of the Coronation of King George VI, when the fantail was painted red, white and blue.

Mr Tomsett, who worked at the mill until well over seventy years of age, in common with many other millers of the time never milled on Sundays however long he had waited for a good wind during the previous week. He had been known on more than one occasion to sit up until after midnight if the wind was suitable to wait until he could resume work with a clear conscience. Milling by wind was discontinued during the last war when one pair of the patent sweeps was badly damaged by enemy fire.

The last major work on the mill was undertaken in 1947, when in view of the damage caused during the war the War Damage Commission financed the repair of the one pair of damaged sweeps. Mr Tomsett then having a desire to return the mill to complete working order approached the Wind and Watermill Section of the S.P.A.B. for advice. The Section suggested the possibility of a local appeal to raise the considerable funds necessary for such restoration. When however, the owner subsequently decided that it would not only be impossible to raise the necessary finance but to obtain suitable timber for the replacement of the second pair of sweeps, he continued to mill for a short period by electric motor only.

1 *Kelly and Co. Directories 1855-1907.*

HERNE

Mill position — approximately half mile north-east of the village centre. N.G.R. TR 185665.

Near the centre of the village of Herne a tall smock mill dominates the surrounding landscape. Built in 1789 by John Holman, who subsequently established his own firm of millwrights in Canterbury, the mill is one of Kent's few remaining examples to boast sweeps and most interior machinery. The nearest existing mills are at Chislet, Sarre and Canterbury, although none is by any means as mechanically complete.

Owned by Messrs Wootton Bros. — R. C. and E. E. Wootton, by whose family it has been owned since Thomas Wootton, grandfather of the above, first acquired it in 1879 — the mill last worked by wind in 1952. All milling is now undertaken by electric motor within the high brick base. The now shutterless sweeps worked three pairs of overdriven stones — one of Peak and two of French Burr via the iron windshaft, the brake wheel, wooden wallower and great spur wheel, and the stone nuts. Each pair of stones is encased in its tun or vat although only two retain their hoppers. The sack hoist was worked by friction with the under rim of the wallower.

To give more power to the sweeps by having them in a more advantageous wind position, the entire body of the mill was, in 1856, raised manually on to a two-storeyed brick base. The remains of the timber staging still run between first and second floor level. A steam engine, followed by an oil engine, both of which have now disappeared, provided auxiliary power on windless days.

Although repair of the cap, and renewal of the worm and cogs of the curb were undertaken by Messrs Holman Bros in 1931, the mill could not run successfully by wind for several years at this time due to lack of finance for the necessary renewal of one pair of sweeps. The miller, Frank Wootton, son of the above Thomas and father of the present owners, was compelled therefore to mill solely by auxiliary engine. With the desire to return to wind power however, he sought the advice of the Windmill Section of the S.P.A.B. in 1934.

A report was made on the mill by Mr Rex Wailes, who also gave two of the four sound sweeps he had bought when they were taken down from Forncett End Mill, Norfolk. The Section arranged for an estimate for the necessary repairs to be made by Thomas B. Hunt, millwright of Soham, Cambridgeshire, and with the support of local societies and organisations subsequently issued a fund-raising appeal. The work, which included the renewal of sweeps and one middling, certain cant posts, and weatherboarding of cap and body, was undertaken by the above millwright in 1936 under supervision of the Windmill Section. The additional cost of the unexpected essential renewal of the second pair of sweeps, constructed by Mr Hunt, was made possible by further support from the above Section, Princess Marie Louise, the Duchess of Kent and from Trinity House, to which the mill was of value as a navigational landmark.

Immediately after the completion of repair, it was reported by the owner that the mill was undertaking a full day's milling by wind; it continued thus, assisted by auxiliary engine in calm weather, until 1952 — at first by Frank Wootton assisted by his sons and subsequently by the latter alone.

The mill has now however for some time been in urgent need of further repair. In 1953 it was reported that certain cant posts were rotten and requiring either renewal or splicing with new wood; the cap, of which the frame and weatherboarding were in bad condition, would not turn due to the jumping of the worm from the cogs; parts of the fan gearing were badly worn; and repair was required to the fantail.[1] Unfortunately plans for restoration made in 1954 by Local and County Authorities, and subsequent attempts at fund-raising by a local society in 1960, did not meet with success. Now however, although in addition the mill requires new sweeps and extensive renewal of weatherboarding and supporting posts within the smock, considerable negotiation by The Herne Society Ltd has resulted in a more promising future for the structure.

Sufficient money has already been obtained by fund-raising activities, and financial aid from the Historic Buildings Council, Kent County Council and Herne Bay Urban District Council, for the first steps in restoration. Completed recently by millwrights Pargeter and Lennard, this has included the

47

construction of a new oak cap frame, of cap ribs and weather-boarding, and of a new fan stage. It is hoped that after the completion of the restoration — to be undertaken as funds permit — the County Council will take over ownership and future maintenance of the mill, leasing it back to the present owners at a small rent. (This was in fact the County Council's original plan, when, in a published survey of windmills in 1955, it selected Herne Mill as one of eight for which it would eventually accept financial responsibility, provided there was evidence of local interest and support.)

Of interest in connection with Herne is that an earlier wind-mill is known to have stood here in 1405, which may even have been in existence well before that date. Mr Harold Gough, Vice-Chairman of The Herne Society Ltd has kindly given interesting references to early windmills in the vicinity of the village — all of which aid in illustrating the Herne milling scene between the fifteenth and twentieth centuries.

From the Treasurer's Accounts of Christ Church, Canterbury, it is evident that the mill had already been in commission for some time, for in a transcription of the original Latin document it is stated that repairs included " the making of a saylerde (sailyard) for the mill of Herne, six shillings and eight pence ". Also included is the reference " 20s. for the farm of the mill of Herne because this year it stands empty for want of a tenant ".[2] Further references have been discovered in the wills of various Herne men. In 1474 one John at Church left to his son Thomas " 3 acres near Studhill against the Milbarrow "; in 1511 the above Thomas bequeathed to his son Harry the profits of " three acres beneath the Mill Bank " which, states Mr Gough, clearly indicates a mill at Studd Hill on the western side of the Parish, as opposed to the site of the present mill. In the previous year, however, one Nicholas Ewell of Hunter's Forstal left " four acres called Melfield " to be sold, which would appear in view of the above will of almost the same date, to suggest a further mill in yet another part of the Parish.[3]

Although from the above references it is clear that there has been more than one mill site in the past, it is not possible to be certain of the exact number of mills to have stood on any one site. As mentioned elsewhere a mill could easily be burnt or blown down and replaced without any appropriate record being made of such. Certainly *a* mill is shown consistently at Herne on all County maps from 1596, while from the early eighteenth century names are available of most millers.

Possibly the most interesting reference to an early miller is one in the Parish Register which states that in July 1589 was buried "Robert Ball the Miller, taken away in thunder". There is however no reference to the fate of the mill!

Millers between the years 1709 and 1879 include the names of Dean, Webb, Kingsford, Hadlee, Hollands and several members of the Lawrence family. the first of whom took over the present mill when built, and the last of whom sold the mill to Thomas Wootton in 1879.[4]

There is, according to Mr Gough, a lingering tradition among descendants that one of the Lawrence family hanged himself within the mill, although confirmatory detail is unavailable.

For a short period certain members of this family also worked the mill which once stood on the seafront at Herne Bay. This mill was in existence only from 1825 until 1878, when it was finally demolished.

[1] *Report to the Wind and Watermill Section of the S.P.A.B.*
[2] *Lambeth Court Rolls. No. 80. Treasurer's Accounts of Christ Church Canterbury, 7-8 Henry IV. 1405-6.*
[3] *Wills. From Registers of Consistory Court of Archbishops of Canterbury. Printed version in Archaeologia Cantiana, in order of above wills — Vol. II Fol. 280 (Archaeologia Cantiana XXVIII) page 101 — Vol. IX Fol. 10 (Arch. Cantiana XXX page 109 — Vol. X Fol. 103 (Arch. Cantiana XXX) page 107.*
[4] *Millers — from Land Tax Returns, Kent Archives Office. KAO. Q/CTL. Herne.*

KESTON

Mill position — next to the Mill House, opposite the Common, on route B.265.   N.G.R. TQ 415640.

Constructed in 1716, the post mill standing at Keston is Kent's oldest surviving windmill. In the wind's full force, in its elevated position near the Mill House, it has stood the test of time well and still houses most interior machinery.

Considering its proximity to Central London this mill, one of the only four post mills to remain in the county, retains immediate surroundings as rural as any in Kent; standing in the grounds of Mr R. Fells, whose father owned the mill, house, and stables before him, it faces the wooded Keston Common on one side and fields below on the other.

The weatherboarded body and the brick roundhouse with its timber roof are in generally good condition, while still present are the tail pole, sweep middlings, and the remains of one sweep; the sweeps were of the patent variety — an unusual feature in a Kent post mill. Within the roundhouse is the massive oak centre post bearing the carved date of 1716, and the supporting quarter bars which are 12 by 13½ inches deep, the largest recorded in a Kent post mill;[1] the crosstrees, almost at ground level, are supported at their extremities by low brick piers. The body comprises three floors, the top of which was for grain and the first and second for milling machinery. Two pairs of underdriven stones standing in the mill's breast at second floor level, once received their drive from the brake wheel via the iron wallower and the great spur wheel with its wooden teeth, in the ceiling of the floor below. Although only the two pairs of stones are present it would appear from circular markings on the floor at the rear of the mill that there may once have been a third pair of stones. The existing stones were both regulated by one governor below.

Additional machinery on the second floor includes the flour dressing machine and the sack hoist; the latter was operated by a slack belt driven by a wooden pulley on the iron windshaft behind the brake wheel. The flour dresser at the rear of the mill received its drive via a belt from a cogged wheel to the left of, and engaging with, the brake wheel. The striking gear once regulating the patent sweeps is housed within the mill at this level in contrast to the more usual position on the exterior of other types of mill.

Although the structure has received essential minor repairs by its owner, it has not undergone any major repair since 1914. With local support and with help from the S.P.A.B. in arranging a fund-raising appeal in the Press[2] and advising upon the degree and nature of repair necessary, considerable restoration was commenced in June 1914 by the Bromley Common Building firm of William Smith & Sons. This included the renewal of the weatherboarding of the body and roof and of certain timbers of the interior framework, and general strengthening of the entire structure.

In a subsequent report on the mill's condition by the S.P.A.B. in 1935, the renewal of the sweeps was not recommended for it was considered that the weight would be too much for the mill to support.

Although in Kent and therefore included in this survey, Keston mill is now within the London Borough of Bromley; therefore although one of nine windmills particularly recommended by the Planning Committee to the Kent County Council in 1955 for possible preservation, this was not undertaken for the area is no longer within the jurisdiction of that particular body.

Milling here is thought to have ended in 1878, for it is stated that a late inhabitant of Keston aged 104 and born in 1865, remembered personally that the gale responsible for the loss of HMS *Eurydice* on March 24th 1878 also severely damaged the sweeps of this mill.[3] It is thought not to have worked again. Mrs Ann Ellis was one of the last people to run the business — Thomas Ellis, the previous miller and owner, having died five years earlier at the age of sixty. The latter is known to have run the mill since 1836 — preceding millers having been Humphrey and Lewis.[4]

Invaluable in their description of work undertaken at both this and another Keston mill are the existing records of Kent millwright William Ashby.[5] (See also Edenbridge mill.) In his ledgers are included accounts for the erection of new sweeps and for repair to the body of the existing mill in December 1836, on behalf of the above Thomas Ellis.

" The contract agreed to — to put up the sails and make the breast of the mill good — £117."

Although the length of time is not stated for the work, payment was finally settled in the following October.

Of additional interest in connection with milling at Keston is that although Ashby is known to have been running only a millwright's business in 1823, he was by 1826 running also a mill at Keston.[4] He does not specifically identify which Keston mill he ran, but it appears from his records that it was the mill, long since vanished, known to have been a smock standing half a mile north-west of the present mill,[6] for Ashby mentions the dimensions of the fantail; this was an addition the post mill is not recorded as ever possessing. Record is also made of machinery purchased for the mill in 1824; this was probably the date of construction, for the mill, not included upon Greenwood's Map of 1821, does not appear officially until the Tithe Map of 1838.[7]

From his records it appears that Ashby was himself either wholly or partly responsible for the smock mill's construction — or certainly for supplying many of the parts concerned, for accounts on his Ironmongery page include —

" 1824. 12 m (Dec:) 16. Windshaft for Keston Mill, £32-6. 1825 1m. 20th. A lock and key for Keston Mill. £-. 5. 0. 3m 12th. 1 Brindle plate for brake. £2-10-9. 6m 13th. Hooping for millstones £- 17. -5. Hooping for millstones 10 - 9.

14th. Started Keston Mill. Flour stones in the morning. Peak stones in the afternoon.

In 1826 a Mr Kilby apparently started as miller here, possibly to give Ashby more time for the millwright's business with which he is known to have continued.

Although it is not stated to which Keston mill the following reference on the Timber Accounts page was made, the undertaking must have incurred unforeseen expense for Ashby:

"1827 5m 15th. 105 Dantzig for Midlen (middling) for Keston. Measured short — 4'."

This is immediately followed by timber ordered, presumably to replace the above;

"1 piece Quebec Redpine timber for Midlen for Keston."

Other rather surprising entries, referring to mills elsewhere, include the payment by "½ sack of flour" and "bill reduced to William Dicker by £3 - 3 for 5 pigs." Ashby's business however must have eventually presented him with severe financial difficulties, for not long after parting with the smock mill to one W. Best he was involved in bankruptcy proceedings. The mill was subsequently worked by G. Wilmott and later L. Olive until being irreparably damaged in the above-mentioned gale of 1878.

An earlier mill is believed to have stood to the south-east of the present mill, at Holwood Park, although apart from reference to Great Millfield in the Manor Court Rolls, no further information is available on the mill.[3]

1 *Windmills in Kent, Rex Wailes and John Russell.*
    Transactions of the Newcomen Society, Vol. XXIX, 1953-55.
2 *The Globe, November 11th 1913.*
3 *The Rev. Charles P. Gordon Clark, M.A. Keston.*
4 *Pigot's Directories 1823-39. Kelly & Co. Directories 1840-75.*
5 *Kent Archives Office, Q/CI. 1/1 and 1/2.*
6 *Mr. G. Smith of Bromley, of above-mentioned firm of William Smith and Sons.*
7 *Public Record Office.*

WEST KINGSDOWN

Mill position — in Pell's Lane, to the west of route A.20. N.G.R. TQ 582623.

This tarred smock mill at Mill Farm had two particularly interesting features — a seven-bladed fantail instead of the usual six or eight bladed variety, and a combination of two common and two patent sweeps, found on few Kent smock mills. Both fantail and sweeps were renewed in skeletal form when the mill was restored — the latter without shutters, and the fantail without gearing to the worm of the cap, or complete blades. Instead of the original seven blades there are now only six.

Millwrights Messrs Thompson & Son of Alford, Lincolnshire, were responsible for the work of restoration which was completed in 1960. Financed by the Kent County Council with the aid of the Dartford Rural District Council, this included the erection of new sweeps, cap, and weatherboarding to the entire smock. The mill is now owned by the County Council with the Local Council helping in the cost of maintenance — a major part of which is the regular tarring of the weatherboarding. It is leased back to the late owner, Mr D. Heaton of the Mill House.

The lower floors are used by Mr Heaton for milling grain for poultry feed by an independent electric motor, while the bin and dust floors above are now silent — sheathed in an ever-present coating of meal dust rising from below.

All main machinery remains intact except the stone nuts and their quants or shafts, through which the great spur wheel transmitted power to the three pairs of stones on the same floor. There are no tuns encasing the stones, or hoppers above, and only one governor remains on the floor below. Both great spur wheel and wallower are of iron, although the former has wooden cogs; once receiving its power by friction from the underside of the wallower was the sack hoist which is still in place. The timber staging once at first floor level at the top of the brick base is no longer in existence.

The mill is one of many in Kent known to have been moved from the site of its original construction — another still in existence being Ripple mill. Starting life on Chimham's Farm at nearby Farningham — the location at which it was officially depicted for the first time on early nineteenth century maps,[1] the mill was moved to its present site in 1880. The Farningham Tithe Map of 1840 states that the mill, yard and garden on the above Farm, was owned by William Kipping, also owner-occupier of nearby cottages, while the miller was a George Whiteing.[2]

From 1826 to approximately 1850 it was run by the Collyer family, while after a few years under W. Moore, it was worked until approximately 1928 by the well-known milling family of Norton.[3] While still at Farningham the business was undertaken by David Norton, father of Tanner and John. The latter became later the first owner of Meopham mill, while Tanner — father of William Norton, also later of Meopham, and Frank — was responsible for purchasing the mill and moving it ten years after his father's death.

The mill was run at West Kingsdown firstly by Tanner and later Frank, in close proximity to a now bygone post mill; it finally went out of commission due to the damage caused to one of its sweeps in a gale.

1 *Ordnance Survey Map of 1805-1844.*
  Greenwood's Map of 1821.
2 *Public Record Office.*
3 *Pigot's Directories 1826-1839.*
  Kelly & Co. Directories 1840-1899.

MARGATE

Mill position — St Peter's Footpath, College Road. N.G.R. TR 363700.

In 1965 Draper's Mill was not only in poor condition, but threatened with demolition or the possibility of removal to an alternative site to make way for a private housing scheme. Miraculously, however, this smock mill with its tarred body and brick base, not only survived the intended onslaught but now stands in the same position and in better repair than for many years.

Preservation of the mill has been made possible only by the considerable work and enthusiasm of local inhabitants. Mr R. M. Towes, Headmaster of nearby Draper's Mills School, so named after three mills once standing in the vicinity, was able with local support to initiate the Draper's Mill Trust in 1965, and with the assistance of Mrs. F. V. Cates, Honorary Secretary and fellow members, succeeded in raising £2,500 towards restoration. In 1968 the Kent Education Committee acquired the mill, finally averting demolition by approving an exchange of the land involved for an alternative housing site. With Trust funds, of which part was raised by the annual Windmill Fair held in the school grounds, and financial assistance from the County Council, Margate Urban District Council, and the Historic Buildings Council, came the first stages of restoration undertaken by the building firm of F. J. Doughty Ltd, at a cost of over £2,000.

This included the renewal of the weatherboarding of the cap and body, certain cant and supporting posts, and the fan staging. Recent construction and addition of the new fantail was undertaken by millwrights Pargeter and Lennard, who are also erecting the first new pair of sweeps; the cost of this will be aided by a further grant from the Historic Buildings Council.

Although no longer grinding corn the mill now has the important function of acting in an educational capacity — the only windmill in the county to do so. For some time local school-children have been able to visit the mill, and since the preparation of the first floor for the purpose, children not only from Draper's Mills School but other schools in the area have arrived regularly to meet and learn the part played by their own and other mills in the once thriving industry of Kent. Chairs encircle a table where various small parts of machinery and stone-dressing tools are exhibited — some of the latter having come from the bygone post mill at Ash. Study of these and the machinery of the upper floors enables pupils to learn the basic principles of the milling process.

Constructed in approximately 1847[1] by Canterbury millwright John Holman, Draper's Mill — first officially depicted on the Ordnance Survey Map of 1853 — was later joined by the other two in the group: Little Draper's Mill, of which the smock was dismantled in 1929 and the base in approximately 1960,[2] and the Pumping Mill, a five-sweep tower mill, which once pumped water for the Corporation Waterworks and stood until early this century.

Among other mills known once to have stood in the area were one near Nayland Rock (previously Nalan Point) in the Westbrook area of Margate;[3] one in the town between Mill Lane and Churchfields;[4] three " Margate Mills " just within the boundary with Cliftonville;[5] and a horizontal mill with sweeps rotating in a horizontal plane, designed by Captain Stephen Hooper, erected at the end of the eighteenth century and demolished in approximately 1828. (See Section 1.) This stood to the north west of the present mill, and from a map of Margate of 1821 appears to have been between Dane Hill and Margate Caves.[6]

The only mills to be mentioned upon the Tithe Map of 1840 were two remaining " Margate Mills ", above mentioned.

The surviving mill, which stands on a site near recent discoveries of Roman pottery, was worked by wind with steam auxiliary power until 1916, and until the late 1930s by a gas engine. The sweeps and fantail were removed once their functions had ceased. The adjacent bakehouse which once worked in close co-operation with the mill when producing flour, is still standing.

Much of the original machinery remains within the mill including the three pairs of stones — two Derbyshire Peak and one French Burr, overdriven by the great spur wheel on the second floor. The grain which supplied the stones was stored in the wooden bins between the second and fourth floors — entry being gained by hatches in the latter floor. From this level is visible the iron windshaft in the cap above; the brake wheel, which is 8ft. 6in. in diameter, has a wooden brake which was operated from the timber staging once at first floor level. The sack hoist remains in position, and was powered by friction from the wooden under rim of the wallower; whenever there was no further immediate use for the hoist, or if there was reason to interrupt the conveyance of sacks to the top of the mill, the contact between hoist and wallower could be stopped by releasing a rope from below — an action which also resulted in the lowering of the still-revolving hoist on to a wooden brake to effect immediate cessation of movement.

Among millers running one or other, or both of the two Draper's corn mills at various periods were J. Banks, known to have worked the present mill in 1847, F. and E. Darby, Thomas Ind and Thomas R. Laidlaw.[7]

1 *Kelly & Co. Directory names J. Banks as miller for Draper's Mill.*
2 *Vincent Pargeter.*
3 *Ordnance Survey Map. 1805-44.*
4 *Isle of Thanet Archaeological and Historical Society, and 1873 Ordnance Survey Map.*
5 *Ordnance Survey Map. 1805-44, and Plan of Margate, 1821. — Kent Archives Office CCRcP37.*
6 *Kent Archives Office, CCRcP37.*
7 *Kelly & Co. Directories from 1847.*

MEOPHAM

Mill position — overlooking Meopham Green, on route A.227 between Gravesend and Wrotham. N.G.R. TQ 639653

Meopham's smock mill, a distinctive feature of this picturesque village, is certainly one of Kent's more fortunate mills. After being acquired by the County Council in 1960 it underwent extensive restoration at a cost of over £4000 — financed by the County Council and undertaken by millwrights Messrs E. Hole and Son of Burgess Hill, Sussex. This included the renewal of sweeps and fantail in skeletal form, the cap, all weatherboarding of the smock, inter-floor ladders and flooring and the staging at second floor level. It has now, in addition, a very promising future, provided that funds can be raised to execute plans being formed by Meopham residents.

Although the County Council continues to preserve the mill by undertaking regular inspection and weatherproofing, it is now the local residents who are particularly interested in getting the mill back into its original order within and eventually opening it to the public. Land surrounding the mill, for many years in the possession of the late owner and miller Mr Leslie Norton, has recently been acquired by the endeavours of the Meopham Society and the Meopham Parish Council; this now enables the trustees and local supporters of the Meopham Windmill Trust, formed by the above bodies and directly interested in the mill's welfare, to continue with the challenging aim of having the mill once again in complete working order. Until then the base will form a small Society and Parish Council meeting room. The ground has been cleared of undergrowth, dilapidated sheds have been demolished, and a large amount of spare machinery has been disentangled from other articles accumulated during the milling years.

Most interior machinery is intact, including certain parts worked in the later milling years firstly by an auxiliary oil engine and subsequently an electric motor. The latter was used by Mr Norton in the adjoining engine house for the milling of food for livestock until the commencement of the mill's restoration. The machinery was last powered by wind in 1929.

The mill is somewhat exceptional in having hexagonal, instead of the more usual octagonal smock mill shaping — a feature shared by only two other Kent mills, both of which have now gone, at Strood and Lower Stoke.[1] Although apparently considered a model mill when constructed, it has a smaller interior than the average sized smock, and certain machinery of less than average dimensions. The brake wheel with iron arms and wooden brake is only 6 feet 6 inches in diameter. The iron wallower engaging with the brake wheel once conveyed power to the adjacent metal sack hoist by friction from its wooden under rim.

Below the fourth or bin floor is the stone floor with its two pairs of underdriven stones — one with a tun encasing it, in addition to the shoe once conveying grain from the hopper above and the remains of the bell alarm — operating when the hopper was short of grain. Unless the bins above remained full, thus giving a constant supply of grain to the stones via the hopper, the stones would eventually " run dry ", presenting a serious risk of fire from the sparks resulting between their surfaces.

The old flour dressing machine, although once at work on the second floor, has now been placed on view on the stone floor; flour, which was milled here until the outbreak of the First World War, subsequently gave way entirely to the preparation of food for local livestock. An additional pair of stones was installed by Mr Norton on the second floor to undertake extra grinding at this once busy mill, and could be worked by wind via the great spur wheel of iron in the ceiling above it, or by the auxiliary engine below. The machinery formerly conveying power from the engine to the great spur wheel to work the stones above when not being powered by wind remains in situ. When this was in use the sweeps and brake wheel would remain motionless. There are no governors present. The first and ground floors are now devoted entirely to machinery once engine driven. The mill is reputed to have made its own electric light, although there is no longer any evidence of this.

Though the mill is recorded to have been constructed in 1801 by the Strood milling family of Killick,[2] from, it is believed, the timbers of an old battleship dismantled at Chatham Dockyard,[3] it was not included in Greenwood's county survey of 1819 and 1820, or the 1805 to 1844 Ordnance Survey; the only mill then depicted in the vicinity was at nearby Priestwood — a mill about which there is unfortunately little information. The Tithe Map of 1841 refers to the present mill under J. Killick, but not to any mill at Priestwood.[4]

James Killick is stated by subsequent Trade Directories to have been the only miller until 1882, at which date he was joined by Thomas and Richard Killick. The mill was later purchased by the Norton family (see West Kingsdown mill) — the first entry in a Trade Directory being John Norton in 1895.[5] William Norton, father of the late Leslie, joined the business with the above John, his uncle, thus forming " J & W Norton (Meopham) Ltd ". Leslie Norton joined the family milling concern on leaving school, while two brothers helped for a short time before the First World War on delivery rounds and in the nearby baker's shop. Before wind gave way to mechanical power William and Leslie Norton would often stay at the mill at night in a suitable wind, milling animal feed for local farmers. When his father died after the last war, Leslie Norton continued the business alone, until the mill finally went out of commission when restored.

[1] *Windmills in Kent, Rex Wailes and John Russell.*
     Transactions of the Newcomen Society, Vol. XXIX, 1953-55.
[2] *Watermills and Windmills. W. Coles Finch. Daniel, 1933.*
[3] *Kent Messenger, May 24th 1968.*
[4] *Public Record Office.*
[5] *Kelly & Co. Trade Directories 1845-1899.*

NORTHBOURNE

Mill position — New Mill Farm, Mill Lane. To the south-west of the village. N.G.R. TR 331521

Of three mills standing in the vicinity of Northbourne at various times in the last three centuries, the New Mill, the last to appear, is the sole survivor. Built in 1845 by Messrs Holman of Canterbury for Richard Fuller, in whose family it has remained to this day, the smock mill was still working by wind with two sweeps in the 1930s. Milling was then continued for a further twenty years by electric motor.

Unfortunately its general state of preservation is at present far from perfect; the timber body now devoid of cap and sweeps has been markedly subjected to the elements in its vulnerable position in high open country. The mill is empty and the floors within are rotting in many places. The windshaft protrudes above the curb, remaining a lone symbol of its once busily rotating sweeps.

The present owner, Richard Mackney Fuller, took possession of the mill from his father, the late Norman Fuller, in 1968 and through his interest in the mill's history has kindly made available certain valuable information. Still in existence and in the possession of the family is the miller's accounts book kept from the day that New Mill was built until the final entry in 1951. Included in it are many interesting details of the accounts and activities of the mill during the ownership of three generations of the Fuller family — Richard until 1881, Thomas until 1902, and Ernest until 1957 — and it is with the present owner's kind permission that extracts, invaluable in their depiction of the mill's history, are included here.

A clear picture of both mill and adjoining buildings is given in an official valuation in 1888:

" Windmill timber built, on one storey of brick walls; fitted with patent sails and driving one pear of Peaks and two pairs of French stones; flour dressing machine and offal separator and a wheat smutting machine. Timber built store; detached brick built stables and a waggon and cart lodge; a fowl house and coal shed and pig styes and W.C. adjoining mill. Dwelling house with miller's cottage attached — each with outbuildings. The whole of the above with half an acre of ground and gardens valued at the sum of £1285."

Details of purchase of milling equipment is first given in August 1848:

" Worked up new pair of Peak stones at New Mill."

In 1886 first mention is made of auxiliary power at the mill:

" Supplied — one 7 h.p. Robey engine; engine house timber built, with galvanised roof, valued at sum of £210."

The accounts continue thus:

" 1891 — started the pair of Peak stones to drive by steam independent of wind power. Cost £50.

" March 16th 1891, started by wind grinding wheat, and by steam grinding barley.

" January 1893. Started new Peak stone for a steam runner and had the old steam runner stone up for a wind runner."

Further details of replacements of various stones are included, while in September 1910 the book states:

" Started engine after being thoroughly overhauled and repaired. Cost £52.10.0.

" December 3rd. 1910 — started mill after being thoroughly overhauled and repaired with 2 new cant posts, new weather-boarding and timbers, and 1 new sweep by Holman Bros.

" 1913, Northbourne New Mill. Nos on Tithe Map, 465, 466, 467, — 2 houses and 10 acres of land.

" Valued by W. Petley August 1925 @ £1500.

" July 1915, accident to mill by whirlwind. Fan and two sweeps blown off.

" 1916 — started running with 2 sweeps. Repairs long delayed.

" 1919 — additional room to miller's cottage, work carried out by T. Denne.

" 1911 — took out one piece of 64 wire and put 44 in its place for dressing standard flour.

" 1917 — Making barley flour with above machine. Barley ground with wheat stones.

" 1947 — engine scrapped. Pig styes in bad shape.

" 1949 — Mill dismantled, stones in stone floor removed. Mill out of commission.

" 1951 — January. Electric motor installed to provide power to drive the " steam " stones." (Work was continued at the mill in this way for several years after.)

Of interest is the fact that the Old Mill once to the north of New Mill also worked with two sweeps only for a time when at work earlier this century.

OARE

Mill position — approximately half mile south of Oare, on the east side of the Oare-Faversham route. N.G.R. TR 009625.

The five-storeyed mill near Oare is not only one of the last six tower mills to remain in the county, but is one of only four mills which are in any way inhabited, — others being Canterbury, Whitstable, and in part, Willesborough. Since being converted from a sadly derelict mill to an attractive home by its late owner Mrs Philippa Hall in 1963, the mill has once again become an outstanding feature of the vicinity and is now inhabited by Mr Roger Jameson and family, the present owners.

The ground floor, once storing corn from surrounding farm-land awaiting removal to upper floors for the intricate milling process, now houses the entrance hall and main bedroom, while above, the meal floor has been becomingly converted into a living room and kitchen. A further bedroom and cloakroom on the second floor make complete contrast to the original contents at this level, for here once stood four pairs of over-driven stones busily grinding in a favourable wind; the stones have now gone although the great spur wheel in the ceiling is still present.

Stairs from this floor lead up to a study, which replaces the bins once storing grain for the stones below. Here remains the wooden main shaft running from the great spur wheel to the wallower above; measuring eighteen inches square, the shaft is one of the largest to be seen in any Kent windmill. The cap, which has unfortunately disappeared, was also one of the largest in the county, measuring 17 ft. by 14 ft. by 9 ft. 9 in. high.[1] This has now been replaced by a roof of completely different design. The brake wheel and iron windshaft are no longer present.

The exact date of the mill's construction is not definite, but would appear to have been at the end of the eighteenth or in the early nineteenth century; it was not included by Hasted in his survey for maps published between 1778 and 1801, but is depicted on Greenwood's map of 1821.

Although situated so near the village of Oare and generally known as Oare mill, the structure and most of the men who ran the milling business there belonged to the Luddenham Parish. The Luddenham Tithe Map of 1841[2] states that the mill, cottage and garden, owned by John Davies and run by a Mr Kennett, stood "in the portion of the Luddenham Parish situated between the road from Faversham to Oare and mouth of the Faversham Creek, being boarded on the west by Oare Creek, on the north by Faversham Creek, on the east by the Parish of Preston, and south by the Davington Parish."

The miller preceding Kennett was a Robert Shrubsole, while those running the mill in the years to follow included F. Inge, H. Elliott, who was previously at nearby Ospringe, T. Hope — "miller, baker, farmer and corn dealer", B. Filmer and in 1891 F. Ralph, who also appears to have milled at one time at Ospringe.[3] No miller is entered for Luddenham in Directories after the above date, although the mill was apparently worked again, under Government orders, in the First World War.[4] A steam-powered auxiliary engine, the base for which remains beside the mill, assisted in calm weather.

The structure gradually fell into its derelict state during the years to follow, but in spite of being threatened with the possibility of demolition at one point, it survived with the miller's cottage and bakery nearby, until its conversion.

[1] *Windmills in Kent, by Rex Wailes and John Russell.*
  Transactions of the Newcomen Society, Vol. XXIX. 1953-55.
[2] *Public Record Office.*
[3] *Pigot's Directory 1839.*
  Kelly & Co. Directories 1840- 1891.
[4] *Watermills and Windmills. W. Coles Finch. Daniel 1933.*

RIPPLE

Mill position — one mile south east of Ripple; approached along lane off A.258.   N.G.R. T.R. 362490.

A derelict windmill is a sad sight; a fallen windmill even more so; but to many nothing could appear more tragically unsightly than the present state of Ripple mill. Having been taken over by Rediffusion Television it now has no sweeps or cap, while the upper part of its smock is enshrouded by many television aerials.

When the Company purchased the mill in 1955 the last remaining patent sweep and internal machinery were removed before the mill structure was transformed into a receiving and distributing centre for the Deal area. Although the smock appears structurally sound the scientific additions so foreign to a mill have robbed it of all original character, and while those Kent mills which have been restored can be viewed with pride and those decaying with nostalgia, this particular mill cannot at present easily be viewed with either. Although the original gamekeeper's house is in good order on land nearby, the miller's cottage is derelict amidst thick undergrowth, while all that remains of the granary once adjacent to the mill are the foundations — now filled with weeds and water.

In 1947 the Wind and Watermill Section of the S.P.A.B. investigated the possibility of the mill's restoration, but although the two adjacent cottages were subsequently made habitable by the owner, no repair was undertaken on the mill. Due to the large cost involved in restoring the mill to working order and the general lack of forthcoming local support, the Section did not issue a fund-raising appeal.

The mill, in common with many others once standing in the county, is thought to have been moved from its original place of construction — in this case Drellingore near Hawkinge.[1] Although it has been suggested that it was moved here in about 1810, there is no mill depicted at either site on Greenwood's Map of 1821 or the Ordnance Survey Map of 1805-1844; this would imply that the mill, if originally constructed at Drellingore, appeared there after 1820 but had been conveyed to Ripple by approximately 1840 when it appeared on the Tithe Map, standing near the boundary with Ringwould Parish. Previous mills are recorded at Ripple on maps of 1680 and 1770[2] — at or near the present site.

The Tithe Map states that the Mill Field, house and garden, in addition to the windmill, stable and yard, were owned by Benjamin Horn and run by John Mummery.[3] Arriving just before this from one of the Eastry mills,[4] John Mummery was later succeeded by another member of the family, Henry, and he in turn by William Mummery, described as "farmer and miller". Some years later the mill came under the ownership of John Henry Monins — being managed by one George Simpson. The business was run after the First World War by John E. Monins, after whose death during the last war, it was finally discontinued;[5] the mill remained unattended until taken over by Rediffusion.

A local inhabitant states that the milling business was very active during its final years — with six men and two lorries being employed for the collection and delivery of corn and meal, although in the two summers before the machinery finally ceased, the wind conditions were not very favourable and the auxiliary oil engine had to be used frequently. Both the above and her husband were permitted to carry gleaned grain from the surrounding fields at harvest time to be ground at the mill for their own use. During the last war a man painting the weatherboarding from a long ladder apparently fell to the ground with the blast from an enemy bomb which had fallen in the vicinity, but was luckily not seriously injured.

A high walled mound of earth, still to be seen placed half way up the brick base, facilitated the loading of meal on the carts waiting below; there was no staging for the purpose.

1 *Watermills and Windmills, W. Coles Finch. Daniel 1933.*
2 *Morden's Map of 1680.*
  Plan of the Coast of Kent from Ramsgate to Rye. 1770. Map Room, British Museum.
3 *Public Record Office.*
4 *Pigot's Directory 1834.*
5 *Kelly & Co. Directories 1840-1938.*

ROLVENDEN

Mill position — next to the Mill House, to the west of the village on route B.2086.   N.G.R. TQ 838315

"This mill has been restored in Happy Memory of John Nicholas Barham. He lived his short life within sight of it and it overlooked the countryside he loved so well."
July 24, 1937 — August 24, 1955.

Placed upon the roundhouse in 1956, this inscription records the restoration of Rolvenden post mill — an undertaking made as a memorial by his parents to a young inhabitant of Rolvenden tragically killed only a short time before. This unusual but certainly wonderful idea for a memorial — an action undertaken at only one other remaining Kent mill, Stelling Minnis — enabled this post mill to be transformed from a derelict to one of the best surviving examples in the county.

The mill, which ended work at the close of the last century, thus managed to survive at a time when its future indeed appeared somewhat precarious. From one report sent by a member to the Wind and Watermill Section of the S.P.A.B., in 1950, and another made by the Section's Technical Advisor in 1956, it was obvious that the structure had become in need of considerable repair; part of the flooring of the first floor and certain supporting timbers were decayed, as was the framing of the breast of the mill and much of the weatherboarding; the crowntree had become misshapen and the windshaft had dropped approximately three inches in position, while most of the roundhouse — apparently renewed when certain repair was undertaken in the 1930s — had by now fallen; only the middling and parts of the last pair of common sweeps remained, the other pair having been removed when work ceased at the mill.

Restoration in 1956, which included the renewal of certain interior framework, the weatherboarding, sweeps, and a brick roundhouse with tarred timber roof, was undertaken by Messrs Thompson and Son, Millwrights of Alford, Lincolnshire, in consultation with the above Section.

Standing on a mound in enclosed farmland adjoining the Mill House, this privately owned mill, once featured in the film production of " Half a Sixpence ", may be viewed at close range from the exterior by interested visitors. The interior, which is not open for general inspection, retains much of its machinery including, on the second floor, two pairs of stones, one in the mill breast and one in the tail, each with a stone nut — one of iron and one of wood. The brake wheel has an unusual brake similar to that of the Wittersham post mill, of iron above and wood below approximately the centre line of the wheel. The wooden windshaft, as already demonstrated by Mr Rex Wailes,' appears to have been reversed at some time in its career — now having the original anterior end with mortises for a brake wheel to the rear, and supporting a tail wheel which was probably added at the same time.

The drive from brake and tail wheels to each of the two stones would have been direct and therefore required no wallower or great spur wheel.

At first floor level one governor remains, while the other, with links and arms of wooden construction — a feature seen only in Kent — has unfortunately disappeared. On the centre post here is carved " E. W." and " H. Allen 1828 " while on the side framing is the name " E. Witt " with a somewhat faded nineteenth century date, and above is a clearly legible date of " 1772 ".

Although with the existence of a document concerning the mill house in 1556,[2] it is known that a mill must have stood here by that date, and the existing mill mound may well be of even earlier origin, it is certain that the present mill is not that depicted upon Symonson's map of 1596, as evidenced by subsequent county maps. No mill is shown on the site on Morden's map of 1680, or Bowen's map of 1736, although one depicted on Harris' map of 1719 suggests that for an unknown period in the fifty-six intervening years, a further mill was in existence at this site. The present mill must therefore have been constructed at a date after 1736 — after which it appeared on all county maps — and it would appear highly probable that this was in 1772, the date carved inside the mill.

The miller in 1834 is known to have been a Thomas Record, while the Tithe Map of 1839[3] names the occupier of the house and mill as Richard Reeves, who is known to have been running the mill at nearby Benenden at the same time. The owner of Rolvenden mill at that time was Thomas Gybbon Monypenny, who from the Tithe Map appears to have been a member of a prominent local landowning family. Subsequent millers included George Bridge, Laurence Foster, John Greenhill — "miller and grazier", and finally Horace Dunk,[4] who after giving up milling turned entirely to farming while living at "Windmill House". No miller is named in any Directory after 1882, and it was at this date that the mill is thought to have gone out of commission.

[1] Transactions of the Newcomen Society. Vol. XXIX 1955, page 223, by Rex Wailes and John Russell.
[2] Kent Archives Office. U409. T42.
[3] Public Record Office.
[4] Pigot's Directory of 1834.
    Bagshaw's Directory of 1847.
    Kelly & Co. Directories 1867-1882.

ST MARGARET'S BAY

Mill position — on cliffs above St Margaret's Bay, approximately one mile east of route A.258.   N.G.R. T.R. 363436.

One part of the Kent coastline retaining more natural characteristics than most is St Margaret's Bay. From the village above with its Norman Church and until the eighteenth century possessing its own windmill, this secluded bay is reached by a steep tree-lined lane, perhaps more typical of the West than South-east of England. The bay is connected with its contrastingly active counterpart Dover, by South Foreland, the three mile stretch of chalk cliffs topped by acres of grass and farmland. It is here in private grounds high above St Margaret's Bay that an immaculate windmill stands; with fine views of the Channel beyond, it holds one of the most impressive positions in the county.

Appearing on the windmill scene as recently as 1928 it became and has indeed remained, the youngest windmill in Kent. Not the milling of grain however, but the generation of electricity was the purpose for which this mill was constructed. Here no horse-drawn cart ever delivered grain for milling; no sacks of precious flour awaited collection by local farmers; and no cobweb ever assumed the flour-covered proportions so characteristic of a grain mill. Certainly in lacking much of the interior machinery so essential for the milling process this cannot be strictly termed as a mill; however, it does have not only the external attributes of patent sweeps, fantail, wooden smock and brick base typical of most smock mills, but possesses the same mechanical principles of such in the cap and top floor. It is therefore included in this survey.

The lower floors within the smock retain the specialized machinery for generating electricity, although they are now used primarily for private storage purposes. The dynamo was removed during the war. The brick base now encloses a furnished room forming an attractive addition to the adjoining house to which it is connected by a hallway; the timber stage at the top of the base and the first floor door are reached not from within the base as is usual, but from a corresponding first floor doorway in the house.

The windmill was constructed by millwrights Messrs Holman Bros. of Canterbury for the former owner Sir William Beardswell, and although it ceased to function with the onset

of the war in 1939, it remains in full working order and is
regularly set in motion by its present owner.

In 1969 the structure underwent certain repairs by millwrights Pargeter and Lennard. This included the repair and
reboarding of the cap, rebuilding of the fan stage, the
construction and fitting of a new fan, fan shaft, drive shaft, a
new pair of bevel gears and fan shaft bearings, and the repair
of the sweeps. Certain of the original shutters were replaced
and the striking gear overhauled. Damage was later caused
to one of the whips of the sweeps when lightning struck the
mill, but this has since been renewed.[2]

Mention of the old South Foreland lighthouse nearby cannot
be omitted here: for two buildings of such considerable, yet
varied, interest to be standing in the same delightful private
grounds must indeed be somewhat exceptional. Although
subsequently replaced by the lighthouse further along the
clifftop in the direction of Dover, in the vital role of Channel
navigation, the old South Foreland lighthouse, built in 1793,
continues to stand in its prominent position, enjoying well-
earned rest only a short way below the neighbouring windmill.

[1] *Watermills and Windmills. W. Coles Finch. Daniel. 1933.*
[2] *Vincent Pargeter, personal correspondence.*

SANDWICH

*Mill position — on route A.257 to Ash, to the west of the town.
N.G.R. TR 322586.*

At the turn of the century seven horses were stabled by White
Mill, to act as transport in Thomas Stanley's milling
business; possibly the most impressive was a white cob which
conveyed the miller in a two-wheeled trap to collect orders for
the following week's milling. Now the mill stands unused, the
stables long since dismantled and the surrounding agricultural
scene much changed.

The last miller to work at the mill was Mr Albert Stanley —
grandson of the above Thomas who acquired the business in
1878. Mr Stanley, kindly relating some of the happenings at
the mill under three generations of his family, recalls his own
school days, when at weekends and holidays he helped his
grandfather and uncles by " sweeping up " the scattered grain

in both mill and yard, and by mending grain sacks. His first task on entering the business at the age of fourteen was to make a delivery by horse and cart to Broadstairs — a somewhat frightening demand of a young lad unused to such distance and responsibility. Fortunately the horse knew the way, for *he* certainly did not! On arrival at his destination the young Master Stanley was given a glass of ginger beer and some biscuits while a man named " Tiny " unloaded the heavy sacks for him. Life at the mill and nearby cottage during his grandfather's time must have contrasted strongly with that of recent years, for in addition to his seven horses this miller had thirteen children, who due to lack of space in their home had to eat meals in relays!

On Thomas Stanley's death, the mill passed for a period to two of his sons — Messrs Stanley Bros; it subsequently came under the ownership of the present Mr Stanley and his father another of Thomas' sons, although it was by now no longer worked by wind. It experienced several changes of auxiliary power while in commission; in an effort to combat the increasing competition from mechanical roller mills of large towns a steam engine was first installed to be used in the wind's absence, to be superseded by oil and finally a diesel engine.

Mr Stanley recalls how, with the use of three pairs of power driven stones (two of which were originally wind driven), they milled not only grain for livestock but, until the last war, wheat for wholemeal flour. Wheat was purchased from a local farmer and transported directly from the field to make flour to be supplied to local bakers. Gradually however it became impossible to purchase only small amounts, for with the increasing use of combine harvesters and the consequent harvesting and storing of larger amounts of wheat at one time, local farmers found it uneconomical to continue with anything but large scale orders.

Thus ended the milling of flour at White Mill — the remaining years being devoted entirely to the needs of local livestock. After the fatal injury sustained by his father at the mill, Mr Stanley courageously continued alone until his retirement five years ago — his latter working years having been spent at a nearby power mill. The owner of White Mill prior to the Stanley family was a T. J. Bushell.

Having last worked by wind in 1926, the mill structure by 1953, when all work there had ceased, had become in urgent need of repair. One of the more fortunate of the Kent mills however, it was subsequently given a new lease of life by certain persons concerned with its future well being — the principal one being Mr Vincent Pargeter who has since become a professional millwright. In a voluntary capacity he undertook considerable repairs between 1961 and 1969 which included the renewal and tarring of the weatherboarding of six sides of the body, the renewal of the fantail, one of the cant posts and the splicing of two others, weatherboarding of the cap, parts of the curb and sills and the erection in 1967 of one pair of sweeps. Mr Pargeter states that the sweeps were a pair transported from Wingham mill in 1961 when that structure was being demolished — the original whips being used (one of which was spliced) and the frames being rebuilt and erected on a new middling.

Until 1964 he financed his work alone, although subsequently the Wind and Watermill Section of the S.P.A.B., after receiving a report on the extent and value of the undertaking by its Honorary Technical Adviser, arranged for a grant to be made from an independent Trust to help the purchase of necessary timber. With financial help from local donations, the County Council and Sandwich Borough Council, in addition to technical advice from the Section, Mr Pargeter continued with repair, with some voluntary assistance, until the structure was acquired by the Borough Council in 1968. With the aid of a local building firm the Council has now taken over further restoration — eventually to involve the entire mill; this has already included the replacement of the timber staging between ground and first floor of the brick base.

Most of the machinery within remains intact, including the wooden brake wheel, brake and wallower; the two pairs of stones with their tuns and hoppers on the second floor; an additional stone, once engine driven, and two governors on the floor below; a flour dresser and the remains of the engine-driven machinery at ground level.

Although the mill first appeared officially on maps of the early nineteenth century, the exact date of its construction is not clear.[1] Earlier mills are known from map evidence to have stood at or near this site and in the town centre;[2] none however were included by Hasted in his survey for maps published between 1778 and 1801.[3] If, as Hasted suggests, there was no mill at the site at that period, it would appear that the present mill was constructed at a date between approximately 1778 and 1820. In the possession of Mr Pargeter is a copy of an engraving of Sandwich dated 1787 showing a mill named Canterbury Gate Mill — a smock with four common sweeps and hand winding gear, at or near the site of the present mill; it is uncertain whether this does in fact represent the present mill.

In addition to the mills of Sandwich, two mills probably concerned with pumping water to evaporating pans in the bygone salt industry, once stood on nearby marshland to the north-east of the town — at New Cut, between Richborough and Great Stonar near the Stour estuary.[4]

In connection with Sandwich there are certain references in the Parish records to the controversy once caused by milling on a Sunday. In 1608 one Christopher Leggatt apparently ground corn in his mill on a Sunday in September at the time of Divine Service in the Church of St Mary "to the affront of well disposed persons". In 1625 the same miller refused to pay a tax of five shillings to the Church for his mill, when it had been "lawfully demanded of him". In 1623 another miller was reprimanded for grinding upon the Sabbath, and further for refusing to stop in spite of the Minister's personal request.[5]

Although the type of mill is not specified, the references would certainly appear illustrative of the great temptation to a wind-miller of a strong Sunday wind after several days of calm!

[1] Ordnance Survey Map of 1805-44.
   Greenwood's Map of 1821.
[2] Morden's Map of 1680. Bowen's of 1736.
   Andrews, Dury and Herbert's Map of 1769.
   Plan of Coast of Kent, Ramsgate to Rye, 1770. (Map Room, British Museum)
[3] History and Survey of Kent, Hasted, 1778-99.
   Topographical Survey of Kent, Hasted, 1797-1801.
[4] Above map of 1769, and Hasted's Topographical Survey.
[5] The Home Counties Magazine, Vol. II. 1900. Page 212. F. E. Robinson & Co.

SARRE

Mill position — north-east of village centre; on east side of route A.28 to St Nicholas-at-Wade. N.G.R. TR 259651.

Gaining entry to this smock mill was not easy. Windows and doorway have been boarded over — the only remaining available entrance being among undergrowth at basement level. With kind permission from its owner, however, a torchlight survey was made, once in the darkness of the lower floors, of the interior, to provide information on the remaining machinery. As with many of the existing sweepless windmills of England, the exterior is now rather unbecoming while the interior remains a source of mechanical information.

Built in 1820 by millwright John Holman[1] the mill, one of many once standing in the Isle of Thanet, apparently later had its brick base heightened, thus forming an additional storey. Some of the weatherboarding of the smock was renewed ten years ago, affording reasonable protection of the interior machinery and timbers.

The top floor however has unfortunately disappeared completely although the remains of the brake wheel — iron arms and one quarter of its wooden cogless rim — and the iron wallower which once powered the sack hoist by friction drive, can still be seen from the bin floor below. Much of the flooring of the bin floor is rotten, the grain bins being the only significant part to remain. The stone floor still boasts two stones, the metal band on one being inscribed —

" T. Middleton, Millwright. 5, Stoney Lane, Tooley St. London."

In the runner stone are two lead weights, implanted at some time to secure a correct balance. The stones were overdriven from an all metal great spur wheel and stone nuts with wooden cogs, all of which are present.

Of the original governors which maintained the correct gap between the surfaces of the stones, one, which was wooden, is missing. Visible with the aid of the torch was the power driven machinery used after the sweeps were removed in 1922. The mill, working by wind until that date, had steam auxiliary power, although the sole source of power, once the sweeps were removed, was a gas engine.

Remembering the loss of all four sweeps is Mr Gambrill, the last man to mill here, until 1940. In their cottage at nearby St Nicholas-at-Wade he and his wife recall the conveyance of the redundant sweeps by lorry to Cranbrook mill, undertaken by the couple just before they were married. Born in the mill house, no longer in existence, Mr Gambrill worked both in the mill and on the delivery rounds. In addition to supplying the needs of the neighbouring countryside he ground corn for a large number of pigs kept on the adjacent land. All basic milling experience from 1914 came from assisting his father here at Sarre, who had in turn been apprentice to *his* father at Guilton post mill until the age of twenty-two.

The production of flour, states Mr Gambrill, was well before his time at the mill; he does however know that after being dressed through silk to sift the bran and sharps, the flour used to be distributed to its purchasers by horse-drawn van. From Monday to Wednesday the rounds included Birchington, Stourmouth, Preston, Monkton and Minster, while on Thursday the van went to Grove Ferry station to collect corn, much of which was from Australia and Canada. On Friday the delivery went to Upstreet and Marshside, while the bakers of St Nicholas received their flour on Saturdays. In addition much of the flour was sent to Chatham Barracks.

There was apparently one marked difference between Saturdays and weekdays at the mill: the former ran from 6 a.m. until 6 p.m. instead of the usual 6 a.m. until 7 p.m.!

The Sarre Tithe Map[2] of 1843 shows that the mill, which then stood in one acre of arable ground, was owned by the Marquis of Cunningham and run by T. Holman. Owned and run in the latter half of the last century by G. Steddy and Sons, and later the firm of Hogbens, the mill is now owned by Mr Baxter. The structure's last function, once milling days were over, was that of wartime observation post.

[1] *Watermills and Windmills. W. Coles Finch. Daniel. 1933.*
[2] *Public Record Office.*

STANFORD

Mill position — Kennett Lane, on the west side of route B.2068. N.G.R. TR 128378

The present owner of Stanford tower mill recently made a request to the County Council for permission to demolish the structure. However, after notifying the Historic Buildings Council, the Society for the Protection of Ancient Buildings and local inhabitants of the request (see section on Mill Preservation) the County Planning Committee made a survey of the mill, and after careful consideration refused such permission.

This tarred brick mill, as depicted in a carving on an interior beam, was built for John Hogben in 1851 by Hill, millwright of Ashford, who was also responsible for the construction of mills which included those of Bethersden, Willesborough and Kennington. It stands now completely idle in a small yard at the end of a tree-lined drive in the private grounds of its owner.

One of a number of windmills to have stood at various times in this area during the last two centuries, including those at Lyminge, Sellinge, Folkestone, and Hythe, Stanford mill is now alone, the nearest being at Stelling Minnis to the north and Willesborough to the north-west.

Although rotting in places, the second floor timber staging encircling the mill remains in place. The sweeps, fantail and cap have now gone. One pair of sweeps was renewed in approximately 1925,[1] the other in 1930,[2] and one of the two renewed yet again in 1936.[3] The cap has been replaced by corrugated roofing to protect the remaining interior machinery. The iron windshaft is supported by the base timbers of the original cap which are still in position; the brake wheel with its wooden brake has lost all cogs which once engaged with the metal wallower.

On the third or stone floor, below the grain storage bins, are two of the three pairs of stones once at work at this level, the third with the stone nut and quant having completely disappeared; the stones were overdriven by the great spur wheel in the ceiling above. The two stone tuns present until recently have been transferred to Draper's Mill, Margate. On the floor below are the three pairs of governors, two of which are complete, while a hole in the flooring of the first floor indicates the position of a past mixer.

The miller in 1862 is known to have been J. Fox, followed by Thomas Rolfe "miller, corn and seed factor" who ran the business until the turn of the century.[4] For information on the mill after this time, Mr Clifford G. Holt, of Stanford, whose father and grandfather both ran the mill in past years, has been of considerable assistance. The latter, Mr Henry Taylor, took possession of the business in 1913, purchasing it from a Mr F. Hambrook. Although the tower of the mill was cracked during the First World War when a small bomb landed nearby, the mill continued working entirely by wind until Mr Taylor, with the aid of a local engineer, fitted a single cylinder paraffin engine as auxiliary power some years later. The business was subsequently passed to Mr Holt's father, the late Mr G. R. Holt, in 1929, by which time a lorry for delivery rounds had replaced the two horse-drawn vans.

In 1936 Mr G. R. Holt fitted the two new sweeps, and middlings of best Canadian pitch pine. This he did, states his son, with his own staff, with assistance in the planning given by the late Mr John Russell of Cranbrook mill. He was subsequently awarded a Certificate by the Wind and Watermill

Section of the S.P.A.B. In 1938 the auxiliary power was changed to a Ruston and Hornsby diesel engine; further machinery included a two-ton mixer which was added in the following year. Milling was continued by Mr Holt under wind power until 1946 — the auxiliary engine being used on windless days; at this date the business was continued by Mr H. Beresford Lye, now of Saltwood, near Hythe. Under this ownership the mill was powered for a short time by wind but thereafter entirely by the Ruston and Hornsby engine. The shutters were subsequently removed from the sweeps.

In 1959 the mill was purchased by M. Hancock and Son; Mr P. Hancock states that his firm dismantled both sweep middlings and cap which were by then decayed and unsafe. At a cost of £700 the present asbestos roof was erected to protect the upper floor from rain. During this period of milling, which continued until the mill finally went out of commission in 1969, the oil engine was removed and an electric motor installed for all milling.

[1] *Watermills and Windmills. W. Coles Finch. Daniel, 1933.*
[2] *Dated photograph of erection of sweeps given by Mr and Mrs Elliott of Rainham.*
[3] *Mr. Clifford G. Holt, personal correspondence.*
[4] *Kelly & Co. Directories 1862-99.*

STELLING MINNIS

Position — Mill Lane, to the south of the village. N.G.R. TR 146466.

Stelling Minnis has an exceptional windmill in one of its quiet country lanes. One of the few remaining Kent windmills in full mechanical order, it has the additional distinction of having been the last in this county to continue to mill under wind power. Worked until the Autumn of 1970 by the late owner, Mr A. Davison, in whose family it had remained since 1878, the mill stands on the site of a bygone post mill first recorded over two centuries ago. Now, just over a hundred years after its construction, Davison Mill pays respect to the men who have made survival possible — those who restored it thirty-five years ago; millwrights Pargeter and Lennard who repaired the curb and cap within recent years; and above all its devoted miller.

For twenty years this smock mill had worked by two canvas shuttered patent sweeps only, the lost pair now lying in their irreparable state in long grass nearby; although negotiations were commenced in 1951 between the County Council, a voluntary subscriber and the owner, regarding renewal of the second pair of sweeps and middling, plans did not materialize and the work was never undertaken. All four sweeps had been shortened forty years previously to clear the engine house then added. The Hornsby paraffin engine, currently in full working order, had since installation been used whenever wind conditions proved unfavourable to assist with milling the grain which produced food for local livestock; latterly however, it was seldom used by Mr Davison, his work having been performed only by available wind power.

This tarred smock has only a shallow brick base and by 1940 when the mill passed from father to son, the timber sill within had rotted away from the base due to years of rising damp and the action of rats.

It was therefore completely renewed and had since been soaked regularly with creosote and paraffin to repel the sharp teeth of visiting rodents.

Points of particular interest within the mill are the personal records of a stone dresser on the second floor, and on the floor below a certificate presented by the Windmill Section of the S.P.A.B. on the restoration of the mill. Dated January 1936, the Certificate reads:

"A record of the Society's appreciation of zeal in the maintenance of these beautiful structures. Awarded to Miss Hilda Laurie, The West Gate House, Canterbury."

A wooden plaque nearby states:

"This mill was restored in memory of Ronald Macdonald Laurie; died October 21 1927, by his sister H. Laurie, in April 1935."

If this generous restoration had not been undertaken the mill would most certainly have stopped many years ago.

The details of stone dressing on the second floor, which were undertaken at the end of the last century, are inscribed in pencil on the cant and supporting posts; though fading in parts much is still discernible:

Barley stones dressed, June 9th 1881.   July 26th. 1881.
Sept. 5th 1881.
Barley and wheat stones dressed July 1895.
Barley stone dressed, Jan. 12th. 1899, signed
T. Crittle, — stonedresser.

Of the machinery within, the brake is metal, and the great spur wheel and stone nuts cast iron with wooden cogs; the two pairs of stones which were underdriven have one set of wooden governors between them; the sack hoist is present and, until the mill ended work, was used regularly.

For a mill remaining so active for so long, the past had been surprisingly dramatic. On the day that Mr Davison Senior was attending his sister's wedding eighty years ago, the mill was not only struck by lightning but also tail-winded; it is said that the cap was actually lifted, although miraculously not removed, from the body of the mill! There is no record of the possible damage caused by the lightning. Mr Davison also recently related how, some years later, in 1917, the fantail apparently became stuck, with the resulting fear of a repeated tail-winding; his father climbed up intending to free the mechanism, but on reaching a strategic point observed it restart spontaneously!

Although the mill continued to function until the end of 1970 it could not deny the change which had surrounded it in the latter milling years. In its flour milling days of the nineteenth and early twentieth centuries, it served many local farmers, often working day and night in a good wind to cope with all that was required. Although those days were never to return, the mill remained proud to the last of its many memories and above all of its mechanical ability and the miller who ran it.

Sadly, Mr Davison, Kent's last active traditional wind miller, died only a few months after relating his milling experiences for inclusion in this survey. A skilled craftsman, proud of his work and the wide knowledge acquired over many years at his mill, he was indeed a splendid character.

After many years of strenuous work he admitted that he was tired, but with the characteristic determination of any traditional miller still clearly present, he obviously persisted with his demanding routine until shortly before his death. The mill, which according to Mr Davison, had in recent years to fight for access to the wind through the tall trees which had grown up nearby, now works no longer.

WHITSTABLE

Position — near the crest of Borstal Hill. N.G.R. TR 105652

Standing high on Borstal Hill overlooking Whitstable town and harbour, the Black Mill is the sole survivor of six mills known

77

from map and other documentary evidence to have stood in the vicinity at various times during the last three centuries. Such mills include a previous one on the present site, two once higher on the opposite side of Borstal Hill, one in the town and another at Mill Strood to the east of the present site.[1]

Black Mill, first depicted officially upon maps of the early nineteenth century, went out of commission at the beginning of this century — George and William Dawkings being among the last to have worked the mill. Preceding millers were Jonathan Rye, Henry Somerford (who appears to have worked a now bygone Canterbury mill before this), James Callingham and later Callingham Bros. from whom the above Dawkings family took over in approximately 1899.[2]

In 1906, after the mill had ended work, it was purchased with the miller's cottage by Henry B. Irving, son of the famous actor Sir Henry Irving; author and artist Laurence Irving, son of the above purchaser, states that as children he and his sister played in the mill and used the canvas covered shutters which had been removed from the sweeps in the making of a theatre in the old bakery nearby. In 1927 the Irving family moved from the cottage to the newly erected house adjoining the mill. Laurence Irving, who had the first floor of the mill converted into a studio with a lithographic press on the ground floor, remembers finding pencilled inscriptions on the interior walls by past millers, of gales and damage experienced by the mill during its working years; at the same time as the above conversions, the mill had weatherboarding and staging renewed and later, in 1935, Mr Irving was awarded one of the Windmill Certificates, which he himself had previously designed, from the Windmill Section of the S.P.A.B. (see later Section on Windmill Preservation).

It was at the mill that Laurence Irving wrote his book "Windmills and Waterways", a log of his summer cruise through Holland, published in 1927; from the mill the author could see his cutter in the harbour below, from which he bathed and fished and by which he had eventually made his cruise to Holland, departing from his windmill home one May morning.

During the last war the mill was employed as an army observation post, after which it was sold.

Today the mill has a very different role — that of Windmill Motel. Under the ownership of Mr. R. C. Harbourne who lives with his family in the adjoining house, the mill now contains the hotel lounge within its brick base, and above, the dining room and bar. The governors once responsible for maintaining the fine gap between the stones are still in existence at this level. The motel guest rooms adjoin the house.

The remaining floors within the mill body, above the dining room, are not used for hotel purposes and here much of the original machinery is preserved. This includes the brake wheel, the iron windshaft and the wooden wallower, which not only conveyed power from the brakewheel down the wooden windshaft to the great spur wheel, but also by friction, to the sack hoist in contact with its under rim. Below the dust floor and grain bins is the stone floor, housing one complete pair of overdriven stones of French Burr and the bed stones of the other two pairs — one each of French and Peak stones. Two still have their quants although all have lost the wooden tuns which encased them. The two flour dressing machines once on this floor have disappeared.

Much of the weatherboarding of the mill body was repaired in 1950 under a previous owner. In a recent survey of the mill undertaken for the Wind and Watermill Section of the S.P.A.B. by Mr J. Kenneth Major, to ascertain the general condition of, and the repair necessary to, the structure, it was reported that although in generally good condition, certain items were noted as needing particular attention. These included the sill at the base of the weatherboarding where damp had penetrated and caused some decay of both this and the bases of some of the cant posts; certain pieces of weatherboarding which had slipped and allowed further damp to enter; decay of some of the weatherboarding of the cap, causing the substructure of the latter to fail in certain places; and rot in parts of the curb at the top of the smock.

Mr Harbourne, who took over the mill in 1961, has himself undertaken certain of these essential repairs, including the renewal of sills and the ends of the cant posts on three sides of the mill, in addition to removing one of the decaying middlings of bygone sweeps, and hopes soon to renew the necessary parts of the curb. Negotiations are taking place between the owner, Kent County Council and Whitstable Council regarding possible grants towards the cost of further repair and restoration.

This mill, fortunately owned by an enthusiast about its restoration, will it is hoped one day return to complete working order. The necessary specialised material and equipment does however require substantial finance and can only be undertaken by Mr Harbourne as time and funds permit. Undoubtedly when eventually the mill assumes its former distinguishing external features it will once again be a dominant feature of the surrounding landscape.

[1] *Kent Archives Office. U309 T34.*
[2] *Kelly & Co. Directories 1840-99.*
[3] *Personal Correspondence with Laurence Irving Esq. Further childhood experiences at the mill are included by Laurence Irving in his book " The Precarious Crust ". October 1971.*

WILLESBOROUGH

Mill position — Mill Lane, quarter mile from route A.40. N.G.R. TR 032422.

This large smock mill with its two-storeyed brick base did not enter upon Kent's milling scene until 1869. It continued to work by wind, assisted by auxiliary power in calm weather, until 1938, after which it changed ownership and was used primarily for storage purposes after a short period of milling by electrical power. Since 1969 it has been owned by the organ builder Mr Tom Robbins, who lives with his family in the adjoining mill house.

Although an estimate was given of the cost of repairs necessary to the mill in 1961 by the Dutch millwright Mr C. Bremer, unfortunately no major restorative work has been undertaken on the structure for many years. Lengthy negotiations were continued between the County Council, Ashford Urban District Council and the mill owners T. Denne and Sons Ltd concerning the possibility of the mill's acquisition and restoration by the local Council aided by the County Authority. Such plans however were discontinued in 1964 owing to the inability to reach any final agreement, and the rising cost of the necessary repair in the intervening period.

The mill is now without sweeps or fantail — the latter mechanism having been sold to Mr E. Mannering in 1946 for Barham mill,[1] and is in urgent need of repair. It does however retain the sweep middlings and all main interior machinery including four pairs of stones.

Replacing a previous smock mill,[2] the present one was built for Messrs Cornes by J. Hill, millwright of Ashford. The timber body, according to Mr Cobb, son of the late miller, was made in sections in Hill's workyard in North Street, Ashford and transported thus to the present site for construction. In June 1920 the mill was bought by Mr W. Manwaring, under whose ownership it stayed for the remainder of its days powered by wind.

During this time the miller was the above mentioned Mr Cobb Senior, a man with the experience of having milled in previous years at Northbourne, Waltham and Lydd. From 1932 he was accompanied by Mr Coltham — then aged nineteen — who still lives in the vicinity and gladly reflects upon his time at the mill. It was from the senior miller that Mr Coltham acquired the skill of dressing the stones — each of the four having varying pattern and depth of furrow depending on the type of grain for which it was used. When all four stones, or three stones and the maize-cracking and oat-cutting machine were in use, all available power would be needed; instead therefore of applying the usual weight to the chain of the patent sweep mechanism, once suspended outside the mill, additional weight to the 28lb would be applied so that more wind power was utilized before the sweep shutters opened.

Mr Coltham states that to safeguard the mill from the frequently treacherous wind at night, the two millers would undertake certain routine precautions on finishing work for the day, often assisted by Mr Manwaring himself. The rope operating the brake would be tied ceremoniously round one of the beams " as if securing a ship ", describes Mr Coltham, and the brake itself secured to the brake wheel by chain — a double precaution in keeping the brake in position for the night. After this a " stop " would be wedged against the striking gear of the patent sweep mechanism at the rear of the windshaft to ensure that the shutters remained open — thus lessening the resistance of the sweeps to the wind. All four stones would be adjusted by hand to raise the runner stone from its partner; the latter would then be relieved of the weight for the night — the fine spacing between the two being set for milling on the following morning. The morning duties would also include the application of grease to lubricate the neck bearing of the iron windshaft.

More than once the sweeps were powerless to act in the morning due to a heavy covering of ice after a " silver frost ". Mr Coltham would then climb up each sweep from the timber stage at second floor level, using the open shutters as steps while he chipped away the ice.

The mill has similarly needed assistance when occasionally the fantail has been unable to revolve spontaneously and so turn the cap. This usually happened either with a sudden change of wind direction from front to back of the structure, or with a change of wind after a temporary and misleading state of calm between. With the wind immediately behind the fantail it did not catch the blades at an angle and therefore did not cause it to revolve; by turning the cap a short distance by hand from within the fan soon faced at an angle to the wind and continued its essential function of turning cap and sweeps.

Flour had not been milled here for many years before Mr Coltham's arrival — the wheat, barley, maize and beans then entering producing food for livestock only. The meal was delivered to various areas of Ashford in either an old Morris lorry, or the horse and van which was painted in " typical millers colours " — yellow body, white canvas, and red wheels. Often milling would continue all night to make use of a good wind, " but, there was never milling on a Sunday ", insists Mr Coltham. To facilitate work in calm weather, auxiliary power was added — steam, followed by oil, for which an extra pair of stones once existed, and subsequently an independent electric plant. When additional power was used the brake wheel had to be disengaged from the wallower by removing five specific cogs from the former.

Great care had to be taken always when walking from the mill interior on to the staging to use the door away from the revolving sweeps. A young girl apparently once stepped through the wrong door on to the stage while her father was in conversation with the miller within, and, unaware of the approaching danger, sustained serious injury.

When the mill was sold to Denne and Sons, Mr Cobb saved certain timbers from the top floor upon which his father had written his miller's diary, and has permitted certain extracts to be mentioned;

" 1909 Chimney of steam engine demolished.

" 1910 Feb. 20th. Great gale.

" 1911 Steam engine pulled down.

" 1912 New engine started.

" 1913 New stones started.

" 1914 Nov. Heavy fall of snow. Spur wheel — new gearing.

" 1917 March. Air raid on Sole St.

Sept. 20th. Peak stones put in by F. Pain, millwright of Chatham."

Possibly the most amusing of any pencil record — obviously relating to an earlier miller — is on the bin floor;

" March 21st. 1882. Ground covered with snow.

High wind. Miller drunk."

Whether written by the miller himself or some other daring person, no one appears to know.

Of the interior machinery the brake and the brake wheel, with its metal arms and wooden rim, are present although the latter has most of its cogs missing. The wallower once engaging with it is of iron with a wooden facing below to drive the original sack hoist. (The existing metal hoist was worked by auxiliary power from below.) Intact are the grain storage bins, while on the stone floor is the metal spur wheel which drove the four overdrift stones below it. Other parts of milling equipment at this level such as stone nuts and the tuns which encased the stones, are stored in one corner. On the first or meal floor are the governors of which three remain.

An interesting point in connection with the mill house adjoining the mill is that Mrs W. Elliott, daughter of Mr Richard Pain, miller at the past Star Mill at Chatham, and her husband, always deeply interested in milling life, were invited many years ago by Mr Cobb Senior to spend their honeymoon there. Mrs Elliott, now over seventy years of age, herself working for many years at Star Mill as baker in the adjoining bakehouse, recalls with her husband, how he and an uncle — Mr Frank Pain, well known for his work on this and other mills — erected the last pair of sweeps here.

One of the well-known milling families of Kent, the Pains worked mills during several generations — including both the seed and corn mills once at Nonington and past mills at Ramsgate (Hereson mill), Swingfield, Lenham and High Halden; while Mrs Elliott's father, who ran Star Mill for many years with his brother Frank, worked for varying periods, some of which were, as an apprentice, in mills at Northbourne (Old Mill), Staple, Kingston, Margate, and one between Gillingham and Rainham.

1 *Report to S.P.A.B. 1947.*
2 *Watermills and Windmills. W. Coles Finch. Daniel, 1933.*

WITTERSHAM

Mill position — one mile north-east of the centre of the village, on route B.2082. N.G.R. TQ 913273.

The Stocks Mill, apparently so named after village stocks once nearby, is one of the only four post mills to remain in the county. Standing in the grounds of the late owner Admiral Sir Edward Parry, K.C.B., the mill, which is open to interested members of the public, is an outstanding feature of both Wittersham and its rural surroundings.

The tallest of the county's remaining post mills, it is in generally good order, having a roundhouse of brick with a timber roof, a white body, and four spring sweeps; it is one of the few mills having shutters remaining in its sweeps and, interestingly, always possessed a higher number of shutters per sweep than most mills of this type.[1] Within the roundhouse, which is used as a garden store, swallows nest regularly and flit among the heavy timbers of the substructure. A notice outside the entrance states that donations from visitors are accepted to help with upkeep although no charge is made for admittance, and that while the maintenance of the mill remains the responsibility of the owner, the Preservation Fund into which contributions are paid is administered by a local committee.

Climbing the steep white steps at the rear, through which protrudes the tail pole once used to turn body and sweeps to the wind, the visitor enters the first of the three floors. On the massive wooden centre post are carved the initials and dates: " R. V. 1781. R. A. 1785, and I. B. 1790 " — the first of which is probably that of the mill's construction. This is supported by the fact that, although a post mill once standing nearby to the north of the village is depicted by all county maps from 1736, the present mill is not included on the 1769 county map or in the survey undertaken by Hasted for his maps published between 1778 and 1801. It does however appear on the county map of 1821.[2]

On the wall of the first floor is a copy of the entry in the Books of the Royal Exchange Assurance relating to insurance on the windmill, mill house and personal property of the miller —

" 24. September 1792.
Thomas Howars of Wittersham in the county of Kent, miller, on his dwelling house — timber, plaster, built and tiled, and situated in Wittersham aforesaid   — £150
       Furniture   — £ 50
On a windmill situated in the county aforesaid   — £250
On utensils and trade therein   — £ 50
         value £500
         Insurance £1.9.6."

This was originally the meal floor, where meal issuing from the stones above descended through meal spouts into the sacks — although it now retains no evidence of such.

On the second floor is the brake wheel, 8ft. 9in. in diameter, which still possesses all 120 wooden cogs. A particularly interesting point here is that the brake, instead of being entirely of wood, is of wood below and iron above the centre line — a feature found also in Rolvenden mill. The brake wheel would have driven one pair of stones via stone nut and quant, although none of these are present; the tail wheel to the rear of the iron windshaft, which is smaller — 7ft 9in. in diameter — would have driven a further pair in the same way, by direct drive with no great spur wheel involved. The sack hoist which was belt driven has been removed.

Above this floor are the grain bins once storing grain to be conveyed to the stones via the chutes and hoppers. It was this upper floor, which, always dark due to the absence of windows, during the years before restoration when access was readily available, served as a retreat for owls, like the post mill at Rolvenden.

The mill has, in recent years, undergone certain repair; in 1958 new sweeps were constructed and erected by local inhabitant Mr H. Payne, after consultation between Sir Edward Parry and the Wind and Watermill Section of the S.P.A.B. This undertaking was made possible by the fund-raising activities of the Windmill Preservation Committee formed by Sir Edward and local supporters, and by financial aid from the County Council. In 1968 further advice was sought from the above Section when one of the sweep middlings broke in a storm; the renewal of the middling and one pair of sweeps was subsequently undertaken by millwright Mr Derek Ogden, in consultation with the Wind and Watermill Section — financed by a fund-raising appeal among local inhabitants prepared by the latter body and by a grant from the County Council. Mr Ogden has subsequently inspected the mill annually and turned the sweeps through ninety degrees to relieve the strain imposed upon them.

It is possible that the mill may, at a future date, be acquired by the County Council.

Among millers known to have worked the Wittersham post mills during the last century were various members of the Parton family — Richard, Robert and Peter, probably related to the Parton family of nearby Woodchurch. Richard Parton is named on the 1838 Wittersham Tithe Map as having run both mills — the oldest of which he owned with nearby Mill Field and the present one of which was owned, with Little Field and Great Meadow, by one Henry King.[3] Other millers included G. Burch; H. S. Hyland; S. Birch; and, towards the end of the century, Thomas Collard — the last miller to be clearly described, in a Directory of 1882, as working both mills.[4] The second mill continued to run for some years after the Stocks Mill, until demolition in the inter-war years.

Of interest in the study of the windmills of this area of Kent is that the Isle of Oxney on which Wittersham is situated was, as its name suggests, once almost entirely surrounded by water — on three sides by the River Rother and on part of the south by a tributary of the Rother estuary; though retaining its title, Oxney is no longer a true isle — the course of the Rother having changed to run along only the Isle's southern aspect. According to Symonson's map of 1596 there were at this time no windmills in the Isle of Oxney, the nearest being in the Romney Marsh area and at Rolvenden in the Weald. It was not until 1736 that further examples appeared in the Weald and the first known windmill appeared in Oxney — at Wittersham.

The present mill and those of Rolvenden and Woodchurch now share the honour of being the only mills to remain in this south-east area of Kent.

[1] *Transactions of the Newcomen Society. "Windmills in Kent", by Rex Wailes and John Russell. Vol. XXIX, 1953-55.*
[2] *Andrews, Dury and Herbert — map of 1769.*
 E. Hasted, History and Survey of Kent, 1778-99;
  and Topographical Survey of Kent. 1797-1801. Greenwood's map of 1821.
[3] *Public Record Office.*
[4] *Pigot's Directories 1826-39.*
 Kelly & Co. Directories 1840-82.

WOODCHURCH

Mill position — just north of village centre; on the east side of the Woodchurch — Bethersden road. N.G.R. TQ 943353.

The mill which exists today just north of the village Church was one of two smock mills standing in close proximity until the mid-1930s. This, the Lower Mill, must have been erected early last century for although not included in a survey of the late eighteenth century or the first Ordnance Survey, it is included in one of 1820.[1] The exact date of erection was probably 1820 for the mill still possesses a flour dresser bearing the inscription " P. Davis, Woodchurch, 1820 " upon its lid.

The two mills are next featured on the Woodchurch Tithe Map of 1838, where they are clearly illustrated standing together on " Mill Plot ", and owned and run by John Parton.[2] John Parton's father of the same name ran the mills previously — from the early nineteenth century to his death in 1831. It is thought that J. Parton Senior may have been beheaded by one of the mill sweeps although his tombstone in the village churchyard states only that he died aged forty-nine, leaving a widow and four children. His son, the above mentioned John, then continued the business from the early age of twenty[3] until approximately 1852 when it was taken over by W. & J. Rayner.

Still in existence, in the possession of a local inhabitant, is a miller's notebook recording purchases of various grains from local farmers, an inventory of milling and bakehouse equipment, and the sale in 1848 of one pair of cloth sweeps to a Mrs Holyer — probably the local landowner mentioned on the Tithe Map and owner of a post mill at nearby Brenzett.[4] The author's identity is not certain, although he would appear to be John Parton, known from Trades Directories to have been running the business at this period — 1842 to 1849. The only names mentioned in addition to those concerned in the actual accounts are Peter Davis, with a North American address — possibly the P. Davis of 1820 and John Davis, both in pencil on a middle page.

It has been stated in the past,[5] and is still believed by many local inhabitants, that the existing mill once stood at Susan's Hill Farm only half a mile to the west, being worked there by Peter Davis before being moved to its present site in 1852; it has also been suggested that the above miller may have written the miller's notebook.

In view of the known past presence of a bakehouse at Susan's Hill and " circular " brick foundation remains apparently seen when the surrounding pasture is occasionally ploughed,[6] there may well have once been a mill at the site; it is also possible that the present mill may have been moved from that area in approximately 1820. There has however been no mill marked here on any known map, and no miller ever named independently of the Partons in any Trades Directory for Woodchurch. It is most unlikely therefore that the mill which stands today has ever stood at any but the present site since 1820.

The above mentioned miller's notebook must therefore have been written at the mill while at its present site; supporting this is the reference included in it to " 2 buckets and chain at well 75ft." which would in turn have referred to the well until recent years in the Mill House garden. The bakehouse equipment mentioned would have been in what appears to have been a small bakehouse with large oven still adjoining Mill House. In addition the presence of a spring at the site of the pond at Susan's Hill Farm,[6] lessens the possibility of a well ever having been situated in that particular locality. The likelihood that Peter Davis was residing in a neighbouring village or in America for some years before 1848 and therefore unable to have written the notebook, is supported by the fact that he was not included in the Woodchurch Census of 1841. A Peter Davies is listed in an 1845 Directory as being miller at Westwell.

The Upper Mill, which disappeared earlier this century, was featured on all county maps from 1769 and must have replaced an earlier one depicted in 1729 on a map of that date of " Woodchurch Place " by Jared Hill, Surveyor of Canterbury. Another Woodchurch mill is thought to have once stood on the existing mound at nearby Place Lane.

The Woodchurch milling business was run, after John Parton, by W. & J. Rayner, for only a few years until approximately 1867 when it was acquired by Mr J. Tanton. He was followed in 1899 by Mr Albert Tanton, the last man to mill here. The final Directory entry for Mr Tanton as miller is for 1924, after which he appears to have continued to reside for some years at the Mill House as a farmer.[7]

Still living in Woodchurch is Mr Reg Pellett, one of its oldest inhabitants who, as a teen-aged boy, worked for a time early this century for Mr Tanton at the mills. It was only after various other posts, including cherry-minding, hop-picking and corn sowing — to earn money to help buy his winter clothes — that Reg Pellett applied for work at the milling business. Although he had previously been earning as much as a shilling a day, the young boy, one of four employed at the mill, found he was now to earn only eight pence. The work was hard for the newcomer and often necessitated staying until 11 or 12 o'clock at night in a suitable wind to assist with the milling left from a windless day. He also delivered meal to local farmers in a small donkey-drawn cart; but partly due to the " spiteful old donkey ", states Mr Pellett, which could run like a pony or take two hours to travel just four miles, and partly because of the work itself, he subsequently left to farm elsewhere for the much increased wage of eight shillings a week!

After the cessation of its milling days Lower Mill was owned by the late Sir Sidney Nicholson, Director of the Royal School of Church Music, Addington Palace, Croydon, and a well-known organist of Westminster Abbey. In 1946 Sir Sidney had certain initial repairs undertaken to make the mill weather-proof, in consultation with the Windmill Section of the S.P.A.B.; unfortunately plans for further repair and future restoration made between owner and Section did not materialise due to the death of the former in the following year. The mill was subsequently bequeathed to the Parish.

A Windmill Preservation Committee was formed to plan the mill's future well-being, while during the years to follow, Woodchurch residents — in particular members of the village Bonfire Society — raised sufficient funds to replace one pair of sweeps damaged in a gale in 1957. Although the erection of the sweeps was delayed when the middling was found to be unexpectedly rotten, a suitable length of Douglas Fir was donated by a Canadian timber company; sweeps and middling were then replaced, but the mill's period of glory was short-lived; the cap was found to be unsafe and for reasons of safety the sweeps had to be removed. With the cost of maintaining the mill in a good state of preservation finally becoming too great, the Parish Council has recently decided to seek a purchaser interested in its future well-being.

This, the only windmill in Kent to be scheduled as an Ancient Monument by the Ancient Monuments Board, now shows the signs of having stood for so long in the direct line of the prevailing wind; the staging has gone, only the middlings of its sweeps and part of the fantail mechanism remain, while the entire smock no longer stands centrally on its brick base due to the gradual rotting and leaning of the cant posts within.

Within the mill the dust floor has for some time been subjected to wind and rain entering via holes in the cap weatherboarding, but its contents of brake wheel which retains all cogs and brake, the wooden wallower and the sack hoist are present; the latter was powered by friction from the under rim of the wallower. On the lower end of the wooden upright is the spur wheel which drove the flour dresser and the three pairs of stones below. At one time a portable steam engine was used as auxiliary power when there was insufficient wind for milling. Large scales on the first floor are now the only reminder that it was here that the sacks of flour were weighed before being stored on the ground floor or taken to the staging outside to be lowered to waiting carts.

The ground floor now houses a large white coach, once horse-drawn, thought to have been used by the last miller, and subsequently used by the Bonfire Society in the village celebrations for November 5th.

The structure of the mill is certainly now in need of considerable repair and cannot hope to withstand many more years of strong wind and rain without deteriorating markedly further. The residents of Woodchurch have enthusiastically tended the mill in the past, but it can now only be hoped that it will enter the hands of someone able to effect the restoration necessary for its survival.

[1] *Hasted's survey for maps published between 1778 and 1801.*
Ordnance Survey 1805-44.
Greenwood's survey for map of 1821.
[2] *Public Record Office.*
[3] *Census of 1841, Woodchurch. Public Record Office.*
John Parton aged 30 years.
[4] *Kelly & Co. Directory, 1845.*
[5] *Watermills and Windmills, W. Coles Finch. Daniel 1933.*
[6] *Present owner, Susan's Hill Farm.*
[7] *Pigot's Directories, 1826-39.*
Kelly & Co. Directories, 1845-1924.

PUMPING WINDMILLS

Among those Kent windmills once used for purposes other than the milling of corn were the pumping mills, employed in connection with certain Corporation Water Works, or for land drainage — as were many of Holland, the Fens, and Norfolk and Suffolk Broads areas.

It is unfortunately impossible to estimate the number of land drainage mills which have stood in this county, for although examples are known to have worked in the marshland near Oare, Stodmarsh, on Romney Marsh, near the river Rother at Newenden, and on low-lying farmland near Iwade, there were probably others which owing to their often isolated positions and lack of any immediate part in village life, were never recorded. In addition, the nature of their construction — iron machinery but structure mainly of wood in contrast to the many tower mills used for land drainage in other parts of England — did not facilitate lengthy survival. Once therefore this work was undertaken by mechanical power many of the old pumping mills would have rotted and disappeared.

Of the above mentioned mills those on land near Iwade and Stodmarsh and the remains of one at Oare still exist.

Of the Kent mills known to have been employed by Water Works were those of Margate, Whitstable and Copton near Faversham, the latter of which alone survives.

COPTON (near Faversham)

Position — Copton Pumping Station. One mile south of Faversham. N.G.R. TR 014596.

Constructed in 1863 by millwrights G. Spray and G. Harmer,[1] for use by the then newly established Faversham Water Company, this mill at Copton Pumping Station pumped water from the well beneath, as an addition to the main pumping plant, to supply surrounding land which included certain cherry farms. It is now devoid of cap and sweeps; the tarred tower is however in good condition.

In a normal year the windmill raised many million gallons of water, although the quantity naturally varied according to wind conditions. It was in use by wind until approximately 1930 when the sweeps were removed and the cap replaced by a six thousand gallon water storage tank. Water pumped into here by electricity improved the supply of water to newly erected houses in the vicinity; in commission thus until a few years ago, the tank was finally abandoned with the establishment elsewhere of a larger pumping station and reservoir — now of the Mid-Kent Water Company.[2] The pumping machinery within the mill has been removed, the tower now being used for storage purposes only.

[1] *Windmills in Kent. Rex Wailes and John Russell. Transactions of the Newcomen Society, Vol. XXIX, 1953-55.*
[2] *Mr. Herbert Dane of Faversham.*

IWADE

Position — to the east of Kingsferry Bridge and railway. N.G.R. TQ 914688.

A pumping mill once employed for land drainage still stands at Iwade on low-lying sheep-farming land. The four sweeps, each of single pieces of timber without shutters, were directed to face the wind by the action of a large wind vane at the rear, while the iron shaft running vertically between timber framing to the pump beneath was activated by the rotating windshaft. Once permitting inspection or adjustment to be made of the above machinery were footholds — pegs of metal set into the supporting framework at the base, and of wood in the framework above, all of which are intact.

The land, owned by the Paper Company of Bowaters, is criss-crossed with drainage dykes, and though low lying is in its unsheltered position completely open to the winds which would once have turned the busy sweeps.

OARE

Position — approximately quarter mile north east of the tower mill, at the rear of the Fertilizer Company. N.G.R. TR 012628.

The remains of this small smock pumping mill lie on their side on marshy ground — the few supporting timbers and a cogged cast iron wheel making a sad sight; further parts may possibly have disappeared into the marshy ground. The mill's presence appears unknown to many local inhabitants and unfortunately there will soon be little sign to be seen at all.

In 1933 the mill was reported to be standing in reasonable condition, with the framework of the cap and all four spring sweeps mounted on an open timber framework — having last undertaken its function of local land drainage approximately forty years previously.

Marshland near STODMARSH

Position — one mile east of Stodmarsh village, behind the farmhouse on the banks of the Little Stour. N.G.R. TR 233604.

The remains of a pumping mill stand on marshy ground on the east bank of the Little Stour. The short sweeps, though tattered, are still in position together with the metal windshaft and brake wheel, which it once turned to work an Archimedean screw originally below; the whole is surrounded by timber supports. This must once have been a very busy mill, draining the marshy ground immediately round it to the mutual benefit of both this and the surrounding farmland.

A long search of the marshland north of Stodmarsh confirmed that an earlier mill once near the banks of the Great Stour, almost certainly also a pumping mill, no longer exists. Much of the area is now a National Nature Reserve protecting rare birds characteristic of the marshland of south-east England.

MILL REMAINS

ALDINGTON

Originally a smock mill.

Position — one mile west of village centre.   N.G.R. TR 056363.

Mr Jarvis states that his father, the "mill smasher" (see Bethersden remains) was employed to dismantle the weatherbeaten body of this mill in 1910, when it was considered unsafe. The base was left in situ and remains today as a store.

APPLEDORE

Remains of two mills in close proximity — one a post, the other a smock.

Position — on Appledore Heath, in lane leading to Mill Farm. N.G.R. TQ 953304 and TQ 954304.

Post mill — the remains of the brick round house are not readily visible but still in existence within a corrugated iron shed on Mill Farm. The above mentioned former saw-miller, Mr G. Jarvis, states that his father was hired to demolish all except the roundhouse of the mill in 1900, when the informant was only seven years old. The iron windshaft was saved by

Mr Jarvis Senior and erected in his garden near Bethersden for use as a crane for lifting wood and stands there to this day, in the possession of his son.

Smock mill — the brick base remains in the lane near the entrance to Mill Farm and retains the inscription — "The Union. Built in the year 1794."

BADLESMERE

Originally a smock mill.

Position — at Boundgate, one mile south of Badlesmere village. N.G.R. TR 010532.

The timber smock of Boundgate mill was pulled down in 1938, at the same time as the surrounding cherry orchard was planted. Today the well tarred brick base is just discernible — having been incorporated into further brickwork to form a large storehouse.

BARHAM

Originally a smock mill.

Position — on Barham Downs near route A.2 N.G.R. TR 214510

A tragedy befell this mill in March 1970; fire which accidentally struck after the County Council had acquired the mill and had actually enabled restoration to be commenced, completely destroyed the timber body and much of the machinery. The brick base alone remains, with the iron windshaft, and the stones lying nearby — sole reminders of a once busy mill, described by many as having been among the finest and hardest working in Kent.

The late owner, Mr E. Mannering, himself spent a considerable sum on restoration in 1956 and was subsequently awarded a Certificate by the Wind and Watermill Section of the S.P.A.B. in recognition of his action.

BETHERSDEN

Originally a smock saw-mill.

Position of remains — within Colts Construction saw mills half mile north of route A.28   N.G.R. TQ 929407

All that now remains of at least four mills known to have stood at various times in this area are certain timbers of the Black Saw Mill, now incorporated into the structure of Colts Saw Mills and its cast iron windshaft once acting as a crane and now as a roof support. This windshaft owes its continued presence to the fact that a scrap dealer to whom it was once sold could not disengage it from its concrete base. The mill's brick base, known to have been present in 1933 and incorporated into the wall of the present building, is no longer present although the date of its disappearance cannot be accurately stated by local inhabitants.

Mr Jarvis relates how his father, who worked the Black Mill, was an expert not only in saw-milling but on moving mills and on hired demolition work. The above mill, which replaced a " six-sweeper " moved from Sandgate, was moved in sections by this miller, also from a site near Folkestone. For his escapades in demolishing various Kent mills, Mr Jarvis Senior was, as previously mentioned, known as the " mill smasher "; many a mill considered by its owner to be unsafe, or no longer a working proposition and therefore of more value as scrap, has been demolished by the Jarvis family. Among those mills thus " felled " were those of Appledore, High Halden, Newchurch, Aldington, and Kingsnorth, of which certain remains are present, and the Black Mill, Headcorn, which was entirely demolished.

BLEAN

Originally a smock mill.

Position — in grounds of Mill House in Tyler Hill Road. N.G.R. TR 125607.

Of two mills once standing in close proximity only the brick base of the Old Mill remains — the mill itself having been demolished early this century.

BLUEBELL HILL

Originally a smock mill.

Position — in grounds of No. 13, Mill Lane, Near Upper Bell Inn, off the Rochester to Maidstone route, A.229 N.G.R. TQ 011631.

The remains of this octagonal brick base stand in the grounds of a new house in Mill Lane. Unfortunately some of the brick-work, having stood for well over a century in its exposed position, has fallen in places, but the roof once placed over the base, apparently as a shelter for cattle, is still present. The mill was tail-winded in a gale at the end of the last century.

BODSHAM GREEN

Originally a smock mill.

Position — on Mill Farm, on the Downs north-east of Ashford. N.G.R. TR 106456.

All that remains of this mill, which last worked towards the end of the nineteenth century in conjunction with an adjacent bakery now forming part of the present farmhouse, is the tarred octagonal base; the smock body was demolished when milling ceased.

BOUGHTON STREET

Originally a smock mill.

Position — Mill Lane, in the village centre. N.G.R. TR 058595.

One of four mills once standing in the vicinity, Miles Mill — so named after the last miller and owner — was reduced to its base for reasons of safety. A bomb fell nearby during the last war, which weakened the structure, resulting in its demolition in 1942. The mill, which is said to have had a large trade, must have been in close competition with nearby Richardson's Mill which was also demolished during the last war. Owned by Miss Miles, daughter of the late miller, the covered brick base has two floors, the entire mill having had five. Still within the base are two large wooden flour scales, once an essential part of the miller's equipment.

50. Aldington Mill
Last worked at turn of century, after
which mill body removed in 1910.

51. Ash Mill
One of last post mills to work in Kent.
Collapsed in storm in 1955 just before
finalisation of plans for preservation.

52. Bethersden White Mill
Blown down in 1937 after being derelict for
some years. One of two once in vicinity, the
other, the Black Saw Mill.

53. Biddenden Mill
After business ended in 1914, mill
base used as house. Remains
disappeared in recent years.

54. Bridge Mill
Last in business in about 1907 and stood until 1955.

55. Buckland Mill, Dover
Believed to have worked in a pumping capacity in conjunction with brewery then adjacent. Main structure disappeared in 1860s.

56. Grange Road Mill, Ramsgate
Having ended work late last century, mill body disappeared in inter-war years and base used, for period, as garage before being demolished.

57. Headcorn White Mill
Once in close proximity to now bygone Black Mill and among last in county to work entirely by wind. Demolished in 1952.

CHERITON

Originally a smock mill.

Position — half mile north-west of Shorncliffe Station and route A.20   N.G.R. TR 205373.

This mill, one of several to have stood in the vicinities of Cheriton and Folkestone in the past, ceased milling early this century, after which it was demolished. The heightened brick base remains as a storehouse.

COBHAM

Originally a smock mill.

Position — opposite the school and behind the baker's shop in The Street.   N.G.R. TQ 672684.

The octagonal brick base which was left after the mill was damaged by lightning early this century, was converted firstly into a store and then a house, for which purpose it is used to this day.

EGERTON

Originally a smock mill.

Position — half mile south of the village, on Stone Hill.   N.G.R. TQ 908471.

The base is all that now remains, standing alone on ploughed land and acting as a store. The mill apparently once stood near the village church.

GUILTON

Originally a smock mill.

Position — in Poulton Lane, to the south of route A.257. N.G.R. TR 283584.

The mill stopped work and was demolished to base-level early this century. Used firstly as a store the base was converted into a house approximately twelve years ago.

HIGHAM

Originally a smock mill.

Position — half mile east of Higham Church, north of route A.226. N.G.R. TQ 719715.

This mill stood in a prominent position overlooking acre upon acre of undulating farmland until 1920 when, owing to damage caused in a gale, it was demolished to base-level.

HILDENBOROUGH

Originally a smock mill.

Position — in Mill Lane, approximately half mile from village centre. N.G.R. TQ 558494.

An empty brick base of two stories is all that can now be seen of Watt's Cross Mill situated to the rear of private grounds in Mill Lane. Constructed in 1812, the mill worked until 1910; all wheels and cogs were of wood and the cap was turned by hand. The body was demolished in 1961.

WEST HOUGHAM

Originally a smock mill.

Position — in a field at the north-east end of the village N.G.R. TR 268402.

During the last war German planes invariably turned over West Hougham after raids over Dover, and Mr Tanton, owner and miller of the late mill, states that on maps later retrieved from Germany the mill was apparently clearly marked as a turning point for German aircraft.

Parts of the octagonal brick base, large metal flour scales and several millstones are now all that remain of the mill; all are covered with brambles. Mr Tanton, whose relatives owned mills at Woodchurch and Lenham Heath, states that after being in disuse for several years the structure had become unsafe and fell spontaneously in 1951. Mr Tanton awoke to hear the roadsweeper calling that the mill was no longer to be seen! Built in 1802, the mill worked by wind until 1926, when one sweep was blown off, after which the auxiliary engine was used in conjunction with the remaining pair of sweeps.

KENNINGTON

Originally a smock mill.

Position — to the rear of the Golden Ball Public House, on route A.28   N.G.R. TR 032454.

This, one of two windmills once standing in the Kennington area, was known as the Wind, Steam and Water mill. Although the water mill was a separate building on the opposite side of the lane with its pond once reaching the main road, both this and the windmill with a steam engine within its base were run by one firm at the end of the last century. The water mill was once connected to the upper floor of the high brick base of the windmill by a covered foot-bridge — almost certainly making the whole a progressive combined milling business in its day.

The late owner had the timber body of the windmill removed in 1952 when considered unsafe and a risk to the expensive apple store below it. A roof has been added to the base to form a store. On the wall is the inscription " Y. D., H. 1813 ", giving the date of construction.

KINGSNORTH

Originally a smock mill.

Position — on the east side of route B.2070 between Ashford and Ham Street.   N.G.R. TR 001391.

This was one of a number of mills demolished by Mr G. Jarvis early this century; the remains were converted into a cottage for which purpose it is used to this day.

KINGSTON

Originally a tower mill.

Position — approximately two miles south-west of the village, to the west of route A.2.   N.G.R. TR 174499.

Reed Mill was tail-winded during a storm in about 1915 when the fantail was under repair and therefore functionless; with the loss of cap and sweeps the mill ceased work. Although most of the machinery was intact within the tower for many years after, all that now remains is the great spur wheel, supported by a somewhat rotten floor above; the floors below this have completely disappeared. Several large timbers lie in thick undergrowth nearby.

KIPPINGS CROSS

Originally a tower mill.

Position — by Windmill House at Keys Green, on route A.21. N.G.R. TQ 647397.

So small and dark was the interior of this tower mill that one miller fell to his death from steep steps within during a gale in the last century. The mill, which ended work early this century, was then tail-winded and the capless tower was roofed over.

The mill house and remains of the mill are now owned by the great-niece of the above unfortunate miller; under this ownership the tower had to be considerably shortened about ten years ago and all remaining parts of machinery removed, for the brickwork was considered unsafe. Now only ground and first floors are in existence — the former being used as a potato store.

LEIGH

Originally a smock mill.

Position — on Stocks Green Farm, north of Leigh. N.G.R. TQ 558478.

This mill fell suddenly about seven years ago. According to the owner, Mr Tomlinson, the structure being weakened by wartime bombing, had been unsafe for some years — eventually falling without the aid of man or gale. All that remains lies among brambles — the great spur wheel retaining most of its wooden cogs; the stone nuts and parts of the brake wheel lie within the broken brick walls of the base.

Built originally towards the end of the eighteenth century near Bexhill, Sussex, the mill was moved to its present site by traction engine in 1928 by the father of the present owner. The milling of flour at the mill was apparently never a paying proposition and therefore not undertaken for long; meal for livestock was however produced until and during the war — an electric motor being used as a source of power.

LENHAM HEATH

Originally a smock mill.

Position — quarter mile off the Lenham Heath to Sandway road, in lane opposite sand quarry. N.G.R. TQ 913498.

This mill, situated high on Lenham Heath, worked in its exposed position for one and a half centuries. Run for some years by members of the Tanton family, the mill last worked early this century. Reduced to base level in 1925, it was used subsequently as a store. Mr Hicks, late of Cranbrook mill, stated that he and his father retrieved the sweep shutters from here for their mill at Smarden.

LYNSTED

Originally a smock mill.

Position — in the grounds of Mill House near the village centre. N.G.R. TQ 944613.

This is probably the only known Kent mill to have had a summer house surmounted high upon its timber smock — possibly the only comparable mill having been that of Shorne once functioning as an observatory. Milling by wind had ceased here by the end of the last century, the summer house being erected some years after by a subsequent owner. Now the summer house and timber smock have gone, leaving only the base. This has since had two large model eagles placed on it, which, surrounded by trees and shrubs, have a rather impressive appearance.

NEWCHURCH

Originally a tower mill.

Position — in a narrow lane to the east of the Church, by Mill House.   N.G.R. TR 058313.

The mill, of which part remains, bears the inscription " Tower Mill, 1840 " above its door; when milling here ended about sixty years later the tower was reduced in height and used as a store.   Both the remains and the mill house stand by a stream frequented by herons among many acres of farmland.

PRESTON

Originally a smock mill.

Position — opposite Mill House, at the southern end of the village.   N.G.R. TR 257608.

During a gale in the First World War, this smock mill apparently became completely out of control — the resulting damage to the machinery making further wind-milling impossible.   An inhabitant of the Mill House has stated that the smock was dismantled in 1959 and the brick base used solely for storage purposes.   Mr Pargeter states that the base is unusual in being octagonal outside but round inside.   Parts of the decayed staging, mill stones, and the old mill cottage are among brambles nearby.

SANDHURST

Originally a smock mill.

Position — in a field to the east of the village; on the north side of route A.268.   N.G.R. TQ 804284.

This was the only corn mill in Kent known to have had five sweeps — the only other known five-sweeper being a former pumping mill at Margate.   Milling here ended early this century, after which the mill stayed derelict until the body was removed after the last war.

SHEERNESS

Remains of two mills, one a smock, the other a tower.

Position of smock — standing on open ground at the rear of the cinema in the High Street. Position of tower — east of Sheerness High Street, in the Broadway, Marine Town, next to Seaview Hotel. N.G.R. TQ 921746 and TQ 924750.

Smock: the two-storeyed brick base is all that is left of this mill, constructed by millwright Humphrey of Cranbrook. Milling here ceased at the onset of the First World War, and soon after, the smock was reduced to base level.
Tower: this must have been situated nearer the seashore than any other known Kent Windmill, for the shingle of Marine Town beach is only yards from the remaining base. The upper part of the mill tower was removed after milling ended towards the end of the last century.

SHORNE

Originally a post mill.

Position — in the grounds of Mill House, above the centre of the village. N.G.R. TQ 689713.

On high land behind the village centre are the remains of an old post mill; the date of its construction appears to have been towards the end of the eighteenth century.
Mr Allen, Chairman of the Shorne Local History Society, states that according to fragments of diaries of Richard Hayes of Cobham in 1776 and Robert Pocock, Historian of Gravesend some years later, a windmill of Shorne which was struck by lightning and severely damaged at this time was replaced by a mill on a slightly different site. This would be the mill of which the remains survive today.
At the turn of the century the mill was converted into an observatory — apparently for astronomical purposes — by the owner at that time, Mr G. Arnold. Unfortunately much of the weatherboarding of the body was accidentally destroyed by fire in 1952, although the crowntree, centre post, quarter bars, cross-trees and the brickwork, added when converted into an observatory, miraculously survived.
The first mention of a windmill near the village was in 1315. (see Section 1, Early Mills.)

SMARDEN

Originally a post mill.

Position — in the grounds of Mill House, south-west of the village centre.   N.G.R. TQ 879420.

This Wealden village, with its many buildings of historical interest, once had two mills — one a smock to the east (worked by Mr Hicks, late of Cranbrook mill) and the other a post mill with a wooden roundhouse to the south-west.   The former no longer exists, while of the latter little remains.   Situated in the grounds of the Mill House, owned by Mr Roffey, these remains consist of the massive oak centre post and supporting timbers in position on the high mound, and on the ground nearby, the windshaft.   Certain other parts of machinery have been transported to Nutley, Sussex, for use in the restoration of another post mill.

Smarden mill, which ended work at the time of the First World War, collapsed in 1953.   On the centre post is carved the date 1871, which, states Mr Pargeter, is the date when the post and other timbers were renewed.   The actual date of construction is not certain.   Home-baked bread was once sold from the ground floor of the adjacent, recently restored mill house — the bakehouse itself being situated nearby.   When the baking of bread ceased the bakehouse ovens were used for cooking the village Christmas turkeys.   Near the bakehouse are the original waggon enclosure and stables.

STAPLEHURST

Originally a smock mill.

Position — on enclosed land directly east of the Church. N.G.R. TQ 787430.

This mill was burnt to base level in 1911, having been idle for many years previously.

SUTTON VALENCE

Originally a smock mill.

Position — half mile east of village centre.   N.G.R. TQ 815493.

The brick base, which is all that remains of this mill, once commanding fine views over the Weald, is now incorporated into the wing of a house built only a few years ago. Miss M. Ward, niece of the late miller, states that after a gale in 1914 the mill was damaged and had to be immobilised. Due to the onset of war no millwright was available for necessary repairs and the mill never again worked by wind. By 1930 the fantail and sweeps had disappeared. In the last war a bomb falling nearby apparently caused considerable damage to the smock, which had as a result to be pulled down.

WALTHAM

Originally a smock mill.

Position — to the rear of the village Post Office. N.G.R. TR 109488.

One of two smock mills once in the village, this mill survived the other by twenty years, eventually being badly damaged in a strong gale in the inter-war years. The remaining base is now used as a garage.

WINGHAM

Originally a tower mill.

Position — at Wingham Well, to the south-east of Wingham. N.G.R. TR 236568.

The lower part of the brick tower, which now acts as an apple store, is all that exists of the original mill — the top having been removed after being considered unsafe. The main part of the tower was demolished to leave the present base in 1964.

WINDMILLS AND MILL REMAINS WHICH HAVE DISAPPEARED WITHIN THE LAST FORTY YEARS

Adisham	smock mill, burnt down 1933.
Ash	post mill, demolished in gale 1955.
Bethersden, White Mill	smock, blown down 1937.

Biddenden	smock, last remains gone in recent years.
Boughton Street, Richardson's Mill	smock, demolished during last war.
Bridge	smock, demolished 1955.
Great Chart	smock, saw mill. Base burnt down in recent years.
Chatham, Ordnance Place	smock, base demolished. Date uncertain.
Doddington	smock, demolished.
Frindsbury	smock, base.
Frittenden	post mill, demolished approximately twenty years ago.
Hawkinge	smock, collapsed 1962.
Headcorn, White Mill	smock, demolished 1952
High Halden	post mill, roundhouse demolished within recent years.
East Langdon	smock, demolished approximately 1954.
Margate, Little Draper's Mill	smock, base disappeared approximately 1960.
Milton Regis	smock, struck by lightning and burnt in 1965.
Newington, Nr Ramsgate	smock, remains disappeared within recent years; main part some years before.
Nonington	smock, remains burnt down 1965.
Northbourne, Old Mill	smock, demolished 1957.
Northwood, Thanet	tower, demolished 1961.
Pluckley	smock, struck by lightning and burnt down in 1939.
Preston, Nr Faversham	smock, demolished 1943.
Ramsgate, Grange Road	smock, base demolished.
Rochester, Delce Mill	smock, last parts demolished approximately fifteen years ago.
Rodmersham Green	tower, demolished 1969.
Sissinghurst	smock, demolished after last war.
Smarden	smock, disappeared over twenty years ago.
Southfleet	post mill, brick roundhouse gradually fallen over many years; few bricks remaining.
Upchurch	smock base, demolished 1928.

Woodchurch, Upper Mill	smock, collapsed before last war.
Wye	smock base, disappeared in recent years.

(Where not given, the date of disappearance could not be accurately ascertained.)

MILLS REDUCED TO BASES (OR REMAINS) WITHIN THE LAST FORTY YEARS

Badlesmere, Barham, Boughton Street(Miles Mill), Hildenborough, West Hougham, Kennington, Kingston, Kippings Cross, Oare, Leigh, Preston, Nr Canterbury, Sandhurst, Lynsted, Shorne, Smarden, post mill, Sutton Valence, Wingham.

KNOWN LOCATIONS OF PAST AND PRESENT WINDMILLS IN KENT

Although over four hundred windmills are known from map evidence[1] to have stood in Kent at various times since the sixteenth century, the total number in the county since the first mill was recorded in the early thirteenth century cannot possibly be estimated with any accuracy.

The documentary evidence prior to Symonson's county map of Kent of 1596 is insufficient, while even with the detailed county surveys after this date many mills must have failed to be recorded.

Such mills escaping record would have included —

a) Those moved at some time after construction to a site outside Kent before having been included in any county survey.

b) Those constructed and accidentally destroyed within so short a space of time that they missed depiction on any map.

c) Those immediately replacing fallen mills and which, when included upon a subsequent county map, escaped individual identification and failed to be distinguished from the preceding mill.

LOCATIONS KNOWN TO HAVE POSSESSED ONE OR MORE WINDMILLS:

Acrise	Aldington	Ash
Adisham	Appledore	Badlesmere

Badlesmere Lees
Bapchild
Barfreston
Barham
Barming
Bearsted
Benenden
Bethersden
Betteshanger
Bexley Heath
Bicknor
Bidborough
Biddenden
Birchington
Blackheath
Blean
Bluebell Hill
Bobbing
Boughton
    Monchelsea
Boughton St
Boxley
Brabourne
Bredgar
Bredhurst
Brenchley
Brenzett
Bridge
Broadstairs
Bromley
Brook
Canterbury
Challock Lees
Charing
Charing Heath
Chart (Great)
Chartham
Chatham
Chelsfield
Cheriton
Chillenden
Chislehurst
Chislet
Cliffe

Cliftonville
Cobham
Cranbrook
Cudham
Dartford
Deal
Denton
Deptford
Doddington
Dover (see Sect. 2)
Downe
Dymchurch
Eastchurch
Eastling
Eastry
Edenbridge
Egerton
Elham
Elham Down
Elmley
Elmsted
Eltham
Erith
Eythorne (Upper)
Farleigh (East)
Faversham
Fawkham
Folkestone
Frindsbury
Frinsted
Frittenden
Gillingham
Goodnestone
Goudhurst
Isle of Grain
Gravesend
Guilton
Guston
Harbledown
Hartley
Hartlip
Hastingleigh
Hawkhurst
Hawkinge

Headcorn
Herne
Herne Bay
Higham
High Halden
Hildenborough
Hoath
Hoo Common
Hougham (West)
Hythe
Ide Hill
Kennington
Kennington Lees
Keston
Kingsdown,
    Nr Sevenoaks
Kingsnorth
Kingston
Kippings Cross
Knockholt
    (Ashby's Leger)
Langdon (East)
Lee
Leeds
Leigh
Lenham
Lenham Heath
Luddesdown
Lydd
Lydden, Nr Margate
Lyminge
Lympne
Lynsted
Malling (West)
Maidstone
Margate
Meopham
Milton
Milton Regis
Minster, Sheppey
Minster, Thanet
Molash
Mongeham, Gt
Monkton

Murston
Newchurch
Newington
  Nr Ramsgate
Newington,
  Nr Sittingbourne
Newnham
Nonington
Northbourne
Northfleet
Northwood
Oare
Ospringe
Penenden Heath
Petham
Pluckley
Plumstead Common
Postling
Preston,
  Nr Faversham
Preston,
  Nr Wingham
Priestwood
Queenborough
Ramsgate
Richborough
Ripple
Ringleton
Rochester
Rodmersham Green
Rolvenden

Romney, New
Romney, Old
Ruckinge
St Margaret's
St Margaret's Bay
St Nicholas at Wade
Sandhurst
Sandwich
Sarre
Selling
Sellinge
Sevenoaks
Sheerness
Sheldwich
Shepherdswell
Shorne
Sissinghurst
Sittingbourne
Smarden
Snargate
Southborough
Southfleet
Stanford
Stansted
Staple
Staplehurst
Stelling Minnis
Stockbury
Stodmarsh
Stoke, Lower
Strood

Sutton Valence
Swingfield
Sydenham
Tenterden
Teynham
Throwley
Tonbridge
Tonge
Tunbridge Wells
Ulcombe
Upchurch
Uphill
Walmer
Waltham
Warehorn
Westerham
Whitfield
Whitstable
Willesborough
Wingham
Wittersham
Woodchurch
Woodnesborough
Woolwich
Wormshill
Worth
Wrotham
Wye
Yalding

OTHER MILLS THOUGHT TO HAVE STOOD IN KENT (*See Watermills and Windmills*, W. Coles Finch, Daniel, 1933) include:

Ashford — moved to Badlesmere   Charlton   Chevening Chilham   Cowden   Detling   Drellingore — moved to Ripple   Greenwich   Kingsdown, near Sittingbourne Lamberhurst   Pegwell Bay   Sandgate — moved to Bethersden   Westwell
(Certain mill sites are no longer in Kent but in the Greater London area.)

Symonson's Map of 1596
Speed's Map of 1610.
Morden's Map of 1680.
Harris' Map of 1719
Bowen's Map of 1736.
Andrews, Dury and Herbert's Map of 1769.
Hasted's Maps of 1778-1801.
Ordnance Survey Maps of 1805-44, 1853, 1873, 1903.
Greenwood's Map of 1821.
Certain Tithe Maps.

*   *   *   *

MILLWRIGHTS

Although the number of windmills standing in Kent before 1596 cannot be accurately stated, it is known that over four hundred have stood at various times since that date. The harmonious partnership existing between mill and miller has been previously described both in the evolution of milling by wind in Kent and under individual mills within the survey. The place of the millwright however has not, for the names of the men who constructed the county's windmills, though in some cases known and thus appearing in the survey, unfortunately often are not recorded; as a result those concerned tend not to receive the acknowledgement they indeed deserve.

The craft of milling by wind has always been dependent upon the skill and judgement of the millwright, for it was only he who could erect a structure not only of sufficient strength to withstand years of strong winds and rain on the high ground usually chosen for it, but of so fine a precision that it could turn or be turned to the wind without hesitation; and with sails or sweeps so finely constructed that they caught and rotated with every available breeze.

The millwright was expert architect, carpenter, and also engineer; for not only did he construct the mill itself but all the machinery within, — every part of which played an essential part in the intricate milling process. Although minor, and in some cases major, technical or structural repairs were occasionally undertaken by the miller himself, these were usually the responsibility of the millwright who was required to return the mill to working order with all due speed, for on this the miller's livelihood was dependent.

Of the many long established millwrights who must have been at work in Kent since the time of its first windmill, none now remain. Hill of Ashford, Humphrey of Cranbrook, and Warren of Hawkhurst, all mentioned in the foregoing survey as constructing or repairing individual mills, have among others gradually disappeared; while Messrs Holman of Canterbury, although still in being, are now concerned only with agricultural and not milling machinery, their last commission having been at Barham mill approximately fifteen years ago.

As milling by wind gradually decreased towards the end of the last century and more dramatically so during the early part of this, only a few more mills were built, few urgent repairs so essential for the continuity of the milling process were required, and the millwright's work became less, resulting in the inevitable dissolution of the various firms. With the increasing realisation during the last forty years of the need to preserve certain of the otherwise rapidly disappearing wind-mills, the millwright's craft once again became in demand.

Although Kent has been totally without a millwright since approximately 1956, resulting in essential restoration work being undertaken by building firms within the county or experienced millwrights from other counties such as Sussex and Lincolnshire, the county has during the last two years once again been able to boast a millwright of her own — Vincent Pargeter. At a time when there is still considerable work to be undertaken within the county on certain of the remaining mills, the appearance of a new team has been an extremely important factor.

Before becoming a professional millwright Mr Pargeter had already undertaken repairs on Stelling Minnis mill and played a large part in certain restoration work on Sandwich mill, (details of which appear in the survey.) Now partnered by Philip Lennard of Essex, he has undertaken windmill restoration and repair not only in Kent, but in Essex at Mountnessing mill, where two sails, a stock or middling and breast beam were renewed, and at White Roding mill, where a new ogee cap was re-boarded after being partly rebuilt and the entire mill painted.

In Kent the team has undertaken work on the mills of St. Margaret's Bay, Charing and Stelling Minnis, and has recently completed further stages in the restoration of Herne and

111

Margate mills; although in being for so short a time it has certainly completed some valuable work within the county. Although the work of restoration undoubtedly involves considerable finance it can only be hoped by all in any way interested in the remaining windmills of Kent that the millwrights' work will be enabled to continue as the funds of individual mills permit, for it is only in this way that samples of these irreplaceable structures of both technical and historical interest will continue to stand.

WINDMILL PRESERVATION

Concerned in various ways with the preservation of the remaining Kent windmills are bodies which include:

The Society for the Protection of Ancient Buildings.

The Department of the Environment.

The Kent County Council and certain Borough or District Councils.

Certain local voluntary organisations.

Private individuals.

THE SOCIETY FOR THE PROTECTION OF ANCIENT BUILDINGS

This Society, founded in 1877, has one main aim — to preserve the county's irreplaceable ancient buildings, and through its Wind and Watermill Section to preserve in particular certain carefully selected mills.

The Society is primarily an advisory body and although it gives financial aid when possible, its funds are limited, being entirely dependent upon membership subscriptions and voluntary contributions. The Wind and Watermill Section has nevertheless by various means succeeded in making possible the survival of many mills throughout the country during the last forty years. Through both its Honorary Technical Advisor and Honorary Millwright the Section assesses and reports upon the condition and possibilities of restoration and preservation of specific mills; it is in this advisory capacity that it works in close consultation with the Historic Buildings Council, the Ancient Monuments Department, certain County Authorities, voluntary organisations and private mill owners. It has also undertaken valuable work in this field of preservation by stimulating public interest in the survival of the country's

58. High Halden Mill
Last grinding in about 1918. A tall post mill for Kent, the last remains of which disappeared in recent years.

59. Kennington Wind, Steam and Water Mill
Built in early nineteenth century with three power sources. Windmill body demolished in 1952.

60. Leigh Green Mill, Tenterden
One of several mills having stood at various times in this vicinity. Accidentally burnt down in 1913.

61. Miles' Mill, Boughton Street
One of two now bygone smock mills in village grinding earlier this century. Body demolished in 1942.

62. Preston Mill near Faversham

Owned by the Filmer family. Ended milling early this century, gradually became derelict and disappeared in 1943.

63. Sandhurst Mill

Unusual in having five sweeps in action until about 1912. Mill body disappeared after Second World War.

64. Smarden Mill

Last milled in about 1912 and collapsed in 1953, leaving centre post, windshaft and other timbers to remain.

65. Wittersham, Old Mill

Differed from existing post mill in having a fantail. Worked under C. J. Banister (miller's cart in foreground) until 1922, soon after which it was demolished.

mills by lectures, discussions, films, an annual mill tour, and by sponsoring many public appeals for funds to preserve individual mills.

The value of the Section, under its Honorary Secretary Mrs Monica Dance, cannot be over-emphasised; certainly in its absence there would be few mills standing in this country today — with a very small number of these having undergone any degree of repair or plans for preservation. In Kent in particular the Section's work has included playing a marked part in the restoration of Cranbrook mill; in the past repair of Herne mill; and in inspecting, advising and in some cases arranging for millwrights to undertake work upon many others — including those of Meopham, Margate, Eastry, Chillenden, Rolvenden, Sandwich, Whitstable and Woodchurch; in 1968 it raised funds to help with the renewal of sweeps of Wittersham post mill by circularising every local inhabitant.

It should however be stressed that although the Wind and Watermill Section has always readily advised upon possible future action regarding the preservation of a particular mill, the degree to which it has itself helped in making such preservation possible has depended very much upon its opinion of the historical value of that mill.

It was to the late Mr John Russell, miller of Cranbrook, that the Section's first Windmill Certificate was awarded in 1935, in acknowledgement of the considerable work undertaken personally since 1918, to keep his mill in commission. Such Certificates, designed by artist Laurence Irving (see Whitstable mill) have been presented to various persons in the country, who have " shown zeal in the maintenance of their mills ". In Kent these include, in addition to Mr Russell, Laurence Irving, Mr G. R. Holt of Stanford mill and Mr E. Mannering of the late Barham mill.

A Windmill Committee was formed in 1929 and the Windmill Section in 1931, after the increasing realisation of the need for a campaign to preserve the country's windmills, which were by then rapidly decreasing in number. (It was not until sixteen years later that watermills were included in the Section's policy.)

The Section had two main objectives:
a) to compile a full record of the existing mills of Great Britain, whatever their condition.
b) to raise funds for selected examples to be repaired and maintained in different parts of the country — the emphasis then being on those still working.

113

In the first ten years alone the Windmill Section handled over two hundred cases, forty-two of which were repaired under its direction. During the war however an increasing number of mills went out of use and eventually fell or were demolished; this was in general due to lack of finance, increasing cost and shortage of materials for repair, the need for scrap metal, and the diminishing number of trained millers and millwrights — many of whom were in the services or had found work elsewhere with shorter hours and higher income.

With no funds available for the purpose, the Section could not itself take over working windmills and although the decreasing numbers had brought a stronger public desire to preserve those remaining, by 1951 only one tenth of the windmills active in 1924 remained so. The Section decided therefore to concentrate not only on preserving working mills but carefully selected examples of those which although now idle were best able to illustrate both mechanical engineering and milling history.

Although for many years after its creation the Section worked primarily alone, it gradually gained co-operation in the preservation of selected mills from certain County Authorities — the first of which was Essex — and from the Ancient Monuments Department of the Ministry of Works and the Historic Buildings Council. The last body was in particular responsible for the advance Listing of certain buildings of historic value to prevent possible irreparable damage or demolition. In close consultation with these bodies, the Section has been able to help owners and voluntary groups concerned in mill preservation by explaining the nature of possible grants, by advising upon and often helping with the organisation of fund raising appeals, and by giving technical advice, structural reports, and millwrights' estimates through its Technical Advisor, Millwright and Surveyor.

The address of the S.P.A.B. is 55 Great Ormond Street, London WC1 and new members are of course welcome.

THE DEPARTMENT OF THE ENVIRONMENT

This newly established department has now taken over all functions of the former Ministries of both Housing and Local Government, and Public Building and Works. These functions include both the Listing of buildings of special architectural or historic interest and the duties of the Historic Buildings

Council — both originally under the Ministry of Housing and Local Government; and those duties of the Ancient Monuments Board originally under the Ministry of Public Building and Works.

The Listed buildings, which include many Kent windmills, are constantly under revision and act as a valuable guide for both national and local authorities in their conservation policies. The fact that a windmill has been listed however, does not mean that it will be preserved intact in all circumstances, but that it cannot be demolished or altered without obtaining "Listed Building Consent" from the County Planning Authority or from the Secretary of State for the Environment. After careful consideration of the specific request in such a case, which includes assessment by the County Council of the structural condition of the mill, informing the Historic Buildings Council, the Society for the Protection of Ancient Buildings and local inhabitants — through the local press — permission is either granted or refused. If refused, the owner has the right to appeal to the Department of the Environment; if permission is granted, the decision may or may not finally receive the approval of that Department, and would therefore in this case rest ultimately with the latter body.

Although in consultation with the Society for the Protection of Ancient Buildings, the Historic Buildings Council may investigate requests for grants for the repair or maintenance of Listed buildings — in which case it is responsible for advising the Secretary of State for the Environment on its recommendations — usually it only makes grants, created from Central Government funds, to buildings of outstanding architectural or historic interest. In Kent such mills include those of Margate, Herne and Cranbrook. Local authorities alternatively may make their own selection of windmills or other buildings to which they consider giving financial help, which need not be of outstanding national, but solely of regional interest, and need not even be Listed. It has therefore been possible for the Kent County Planning Committee and certain Borough or District Councils to be more immediately involved with such help within the county than the above Central Authority.

Ancient Monuments scheduled by the Ancient Monuments Board, unlike most Listed buildings, are usually uninhabited — such as castles, earthworks or ruins of historical interest, although windmills may fall equally well into either category. Occasionally a windmill or other building of historic interest may be both a Scheduled Monument *and* Listed, eg. Wood-

115

church mill — although in such a case the building is primarily under the protection of the Ancient Monuments Board.

THE KENT COUNTY COUNCIL

The policy of the County Council regarding the acquisition, preservation and restoration of mills is based upon a survey of Kent windmills made in 1955, and the subsequent careful selection of nine mills which were made the subject of special recommendations to the County Planning Committee. It stressed then that " the arrangements now contemplated may have to be varied in the light of changing circumstances " and this has in fact in some cases been so. It also stated however that " it is now County Council policy to preserve the windmills it has carefully selected if practicable ".

It has in fact to date acquired six windmills — although one, at Barham, is no longer in existence; of the remainder — at Meopham, Chillenden, West Kingsdown, Cranbrook and Margate (the latter under the County Education Committee) — the County Council has restored the first three, and made substantial contributions towards the cost of restoration of those at Cranbrook and Margate. It may at a future date acquire the mills of Herne, Stelling Minnis and Wittersham — the last of which it helped to restore. Although the County Council does wish to retain a number of selected mills it is usually very keen that before financial negotiations are commenced in respect of their acquisition a certain degree of local enthusiasm and support must be forthcoming.

The recommendations to the Planning Committee in 1955, upon which the above policy is based, were the subject of a booklet published at that time by the County Council and prepared by County Planning Officer James W. R. Adams — *Windmills in Kent*. This showed that following a survey of Kent windmills, the nine carefully selected for preservation were characteristic examples of post and smock mills distributed as evenly as possible in West, Mid, and East Kent; no example could be found of a tower mill which was of sufficient interest to justify preservation. Of the nine selected — Ash, Barham, Chillenden, Cranbrook, Herne, Keston, West Kingsdown, Willesborough and Wittersham — the first and second no longer exist, Ash having been blown down in a gale before restoration could be undertaken, and the second having been accidentally destroyed by fire to base level while being

116

restored; Keston is now in the London Borough of Bromley and no longer under the Kent County Council, while plans for Willesborough made in 1955 did not materialise due to the decision of the owner of that time to make his own arrangements for the mill's welfare; subsequent plans between owner, County and Local Councils were eventually discontinued. (See Willesborough mill.) The remainder are discussed in detail in the survey.

BOROUGH, URBAN OR RURAL DISTRICT COUNCILS

In certain circumstances Local Councils have made their own contribution towards the well-being of a windmill in the vicinity, either in conjunction with the County Council, e.g. Cranbrook and West Kingsdown mills, or independently as at Sandwich; here after considerable past restoration undertaken in a voluntary capacity with the aid of Local County Council grants and local subscriptions, the Sandwich Borough Council took over possession of the mill and plan further restoration.

VOLUNTARY ORGANISATIONS

Concerned with the raising of funds towards the preservation of their own local mills are The Herne Society Ltd, The Draper's Mill Trust at Margate, The Windmill Trust at Meopham and The Windmill Preservation Fund administered by a local committee at Wittersham. Such organisations are invaluable, for the extent of help and interest eventually arising from outside the locality is very dependent upon the degree of initial local interest and support.

PRIVATE OWNERS OF WINDMILLS

Last, but by no means least in the preservation of Kent windmills, is the part played by the individual private owner or person otherwise interested in a mill. Examples include Rolvenden mill where restoration was made possible by a local resident; Wittersham mill restored by the late owner with the additional help previously mentioned; and Stelling Minnis mill — previously described. Many others have undergone varying degrees of repair by their owners including mills at Bidborough, Canterbury, Charing, Keston, Sarre, Whitstable and Willesborough.

RECENT DEVELOPMENTS—SPRING 1978

Herne Mill. One new pair of sweeps has been fitted and many of the smock timbers strengthened or renewed. Further restoration will include the renewal of staging, repair of fantail gearing and continuation of work on structural timbers. Mill Open Days during certain summer weekends under The Herne Society.

Margate, Draper's Mill. With two new pairs of patent sweeps, brake wheel re-cogged, a new stage and much internal machinery renewed, the mill is in full working order and periodically grinds corn. Open Days during summer months under The Draper's Mill Trust.

Meopham Mill. Much of the mechanism has been renewed or repaired, including a new fantail and complete renewal of brakewheel cogs. Rotting sail middlings are to be replaced by those of steel. Open Days during certain summer weekends under The Meopham Windmill Trust and The Friends of Meopham Mill.

Northbourne Mill. Converted for use as a silversmith's workshop and dwelling.

Sandwich Mill. The fantail, sweeps, stage and many internal timbers and weatherboarding have been renewed. Although not in full working order all internal machinery is intact. The mill may be open to visitors in the near future.

Stelling Minnis Mill. Now owned by Kent County Council, the mill has been completely restored. Maintained structurally by the KCC and internally by members of both East Kent Mills Group and Stelling Minnis Parish Council who jointly operate Open Days during summer weekends. The Group, under Chairman Paul Jarvis, is preparing the paraffin engine to power the mill for grinding demonstrations to members as tree growth makes grinding by wind impractical.

Woodchurch Mill. Ashford Borough Council is to finance a holding operation while possible restoration plans are considered.

The EAST KENT MILLS GROUP. Formed in 1974 as part of the Wind and Watermill Section of the Society for the Protection of Ancient Buildings for the study and preservation of wind and watermills in East Kent. One of the most important aspects to date has been its involvement in the restoration of Stelling Minnis Mill. Address for details of membership, regular meetings and of mills open on specific days or by appointment available from the above Society at 55, Great Ormond St, London,W.C.1.

118

GLOSSARY

BRAKEWHEEL: wheel mounted on the windshaft to drive the wallower; the brake band contracts on its wooden rim to stop the mill.

CANT POST: strong wooden corner posts of a smock mill, canted inwards as they rise.

CROSS-TREES: two horizontal beams at right angles, forming part of the post mill substructure and supporting the quarter bars.

CROWNTREE: a horizontal beam forming part of the second floor flooring of the post mill body, which revolved on top of the centre post.

CURB: circular track at the top of the smock or tower mill on which the cap turned.

DUST FLOOR: top floor of a smock or tower mill.

FANTAIL: a vertical wind-wheel of six to eight vanes, mounted on staging behind the cap, automatically turning the cap and sweeps to face the wind.

FLOUR DRESSING MACHINE: machine to separate flour from sharps and bran.

GOVERNOR: automatic regulator to maintain the correct gap between the millstones, as the wind speed changed.

GRAIN BINS: wooden compartments for the storage of grain, usually on the top floor.

GREAT SPUR WHEEL: the main driving wheel mounted on the upright shaft to transmit power through the stone nuts to the millstones, either above them (giving overdrift stones) or below them (giving underdrift stones)

HOPPER: large wooden funnel resting on the horse or framework above the casing, supplying grain to the stones below.

MEAL FLOOR: floor with meal bins receiving freshly ground meal through meal spouts from the stones above.

MIDDLING: tapered sweep or sail stock passing through the poll end and carrying a pair of sweeps or sails.

POLL END: cast iron sockets or canister at the outer end of the windshaft to hold the stocks or middlings.

POST: vertical timber post on which the body of the post mill was mounted and turned to face the wind.

QUANT: vertical four-sided spindle driving the runner stone from above.

QUARTER BARS: four wooden struts in the post mill sub-structure running upwards diagonally from the cross-trees to support the centre post.

SWEEPS OR SAILS:
    Common: sweeps spread with sail-cloth, each being set separately across the sweep frame to suit varying wind conditions.
    Spring: sweeps with hinged shutters which opened or closed according to the setting of the spring-loaded lever on each sweep.
    Patent: sweeps with shutters adjusted automatically by the weighted striking rod passing through the windshaft.

STAGE: platform round the exterior of smock or tower mills from which sweeps could be adjusted by hand and carts could be loaded with sacks.

STONE NUT: small cogged wheel transmitting power to the runner stones from the great spur wheel in smock or tower mills, and, when present in the post mill, from the wallower and brake wheel.

STONES:
    Derbyshire Peak: of millstone grit quarried in one piece in the Derbyshire Peak District, used for grinding barley, oats and maize.
    French Burr: millstone formed by many separate pieces of stone imported from France; used for grinding wheat.
    runner: upper or rotating stone of a pair.
    bed: lower stone of a pair, fixed to the floor.
    overdrift
    underdrift } see great spur wheel.

STONE DRESSING: preparation of the grinding surface of a mill stone by cutting the furrows running radially from the centre, to grind and direct the grain.

STRIKING GEAR: a mechanism to open the shutters of the sweeps automatically at a certain wind pressure, employing a striking rod running through the hollow windshaft, operated by weights on an endless chain behind the mill; a wind force greater than the effect of the weight would raise the latter and open the shutters.

TAIL WHEEL: wheel mounted on the rear of the windshaft in some post mills, by which a second pair of stones could be driven.

TAIL WINDING: occurred when the wind's full force caught the sweeps from behind owing to the failure of the fantail, in turn due to a temporary seizure of the mechanism or sudden change of wind direction.

TUN, STONE: wooden casing or vat enclosing the millstones.

WALLOWER: the bevel pinion fixed to the top of the upright shaft, which engages with the brake wheel and transmits power to the runner stone.

WHIP: principal longitudinal timber of the sail or sweep, bolted to the face of the stock or middling.

WINDSHAFT: shaft of wood or cast iron entering the cap (or body of the post mill) at a small angle to the horizontal, supporting at its outer end the sweeps which turned it and upon which the entire milling mechanism was dependent.

BIBLIOGRAPHY

SECTION 1

H. S. Bennett. *Life on the English Manor*. Cambridge
University Press, 1937.
Richard Bennett and John Elton. *History of Corn Milling*.
Simpkin Marshall, 1899. 4 Volumes, particular reference to
1 and 2.
F. R. H. Du Boulay. *The Lordship of Canterbury*. Nelson, 1966.
C. W. Chalklin. *Seventeenth Century Kent*. Longmans, 1965.
W. Coles Finch. *Watermills and Windmills*. Daniel, 1933.
Frank Jessup. *A History of Kent*. Darwen Finlayson, 1957.
E. F. Lincoln. *The Heritage of Kent*. Oldbourne, 1966.
Lynn White, Jr. *Medieval Technology and Social Change*.
Oxford University Press, 1962.
Ralph A. Whitlock. *A Short History of Farming in Britain*.
John Baker, 1965.
Victoria County History of Kent. 1908-32. Volume 3.

SECTION 2

W. Coles Finch. *Watermills and Windmills*. C. W. Daniel, 1933.
Rex Wailes. *The English Windmill*. Routledge and Kegan
Paul, 1954.
Windmills in England. Architectural Press, 1948. Reprinted
Charles Skilton, 1973.
"Some Windmill Fallacies", *Transactions of the New-
comen Society*, Vol. XXXII. 1959-60.
Rex Wailes and John Russell, "Windmills in Kent", *Trans-
actions of the Newcomen Society*, Vol. XXIX, 1953-5.

James W. R. Adams. *Windmills in Kent* (booklet). Kent
County Council, 1955.
M. I. Batten. *English Windmills*. Vol. I. Architectural Press,
1930.
Richard Bennett and John Elton. *History of Corn Milling*.
Simpkin Marshall, 1899.
F. C. Clark, *Kentish Fire*. Adams and Son, 1947.
K. G. Farries and M. T. Mason. *Windmills of Surrey and Inner
London*. Charles Skilton, 1966.
W. Coles Finch. *Life in Rural England*. Daniel, c.1930.
Watermills and Windmills. Daniel, 1933
Stanley Freese. *Windmills and Millwrighting*. Cambridge
University Press, 1957.

Peter Hemming. *Windmills in Sussex.* Daniel, 1936.

R. Thurston Hopkins. *Old Watermills and Windmills.* Philip Allan, c. 1930.

J. B. Paddon, *Windmills in Kent,* South Eastern Gazette, 1926.

John Reynolds. *Windmills and Watermills.* Evelyn, 1970.

John Salmon. "Windmills in Medieval Art", *Journal of the Archaeological Association.* Third Series. Vol. VI, 1941

C. P. Skilton. *British Windmills and Watermills.* Collins, 1947.

INDEX

(Locations of windmills known or thought to have stood in Kent listed on pages 107-9 have not been indexed unless they are additionally referred to in the text.)

125